# City Spaces

**Program Authors**
Richard L. Allington
Camille L. Z. Blachowicz
Ronald L. Cramer
Patricia M. Cunningham
G. Yvonne Pérez
Constance Frazier Robinson
Sam Leaton Sebesta
Richard G. Smith
Robert J. Tierney

**Instructional Consultant**
John C. Manning

**Program Consultants**
Jesús Cortez
Alfredo Schifini
Robert E. Slavin

**Critic Readers**
Martha Ann Dulin
Adriana Goodier
Dorothy Kern
Betty Liddicoat
Georgina G. Lowenberg
Bob Mudrovic

**Scott, Foresman
and Company**

Editorial Offices:
Glenview, Illinois

Regional Offices:
Sunnyvale, California
Tucker, Georgia
Glenview, Illinois
Oakland, New Jersey
Carrollton, Texas

Scott, Foresman Reading: An American Tradition

Gold Medal Printing

# Acknowledgments

## Text

Page 9: The inclusion of *Mitchell Is Moving* by Marjorie Weinman Sharmat (text) copyright © 1978 by Marjorie Weinman Sharmat, illustrations copyright © 1978 by Jose Aruego and Ariane Dewey; is reprinted by arrangement with Macmillan Publishing Company.
Page 27: *Just the Thing for Geraldine* by Ellen Conford. Text copyright © 1974 by Ellen Conford. Reprinted by permission of Little, Brown and Company, and McIntosh & Otis, Inc.
Page 45: Complete text, abridged and adapted from *How Far Felipe?* by Genevieve Gray. Text copyright © 1978 by Genevieve Gray. Reprinted by permission of Harper & Row, Publishers, Inc.
Page 73: "How to Tell a Tiger" from *You Read to Me, I'll Read to You* by John Ciardi (J. B. Lippincott). Copyright © 1962 by John Ciardi. Reprinted by permission of Harper & Row, Publishers, Inc.
Page 74: "There Was a Young Lady of Riga," anonymous, from *A Very First Poetry Book*.
Page 74: "Tiger" by Mary Ann Hoberman from *Hello and Good-by*. Reprinted by permission of Russell & Volkening, Inc. as agents for the author. Copyright © 1959 by Mary Ann Hoberman.
Page 77: First stanza from "City" by Langston Hughes. Reprinted by permission of Harold Ober Associates Incorporated. Copyright © 1958 by Langston Hughes.
Page 81: Adaptation of *Peter's Brownstone House* by Hila Colman (text only). Copyright © 1963 by Hila Colman. By permission of William Morrow & Company.
Page 114: "Catching Quiet" by Marci Ridlon. Copyright © 1982 by Marci Ridlon. Reprinted by permission of the author.
Page 115: *The Loudest Noise in the World* by Benjamin Elkin. Copyright 1954, renewed © 1982 by Benjamin Elkin. Adapted by permission of Viking Penguin Inc.
Page 136: From *The World Book Encyclopedia*. Copyright © 1985 World Book, Inc. Reprinted by permission.
Page 151: *Fiona's Flea* by Beverly Keller. Copyright © 1981 by Beverly Keller. Adapted by permission of the author c/o Edite Kroll.
Page 167: "Philbert Phlurk" from *The Sheriff of Rottenshot* by Jack Prelutsky. Copyright © 1982 by Jack Prelutsky. By permission of Greenwillow Books (A Division of William Morrow & Company).

Page 168: "Yertle the Turtle," with specified punctuation changes and accompanying illustrations, Copyright 1951, © 1958 by Dr. Seuss. Reprinted from *Yertle the Turtle and Other Stories* by Dr. Seuss, by permission of Random House, Inc.
Page 191: From *Pecos Bill Rides a Tornado* by Wyatt Blassingame. Copyright © 1973 by Wyatt Blassingame. Reprinted with the permission of Garrard Publishing Company, Champaign, Illinois.
Page 206: "Go Wind" from *I Feel the Same Way* by Lilian Moore. Copyright © 1967 by Lilian Moore. Published by Atheneum. Reprinted by permission of the author. All rights reserved.
Page 209: *Track Is for Me* by Lowell A. Dickmeyer. Copyright © 1979 by Lerner Publications Company. Adapted by permission of Lerner Publications Company, 241 First Avenue North, Minneapolis, Minnesota 55401.
Page 247: From *Old, Older, Oldest* by Lenore Klein. Copyright © 1983 by Lenore Klein. Reprinted by permission of the author.
Page 259: "The Origami Truce" adapted from *Lucky Charms & Birthday Wishes* by Christine McDonnell. Text copyright © 1984 by Christine McDonnell. Reprinted by permission of Viking Penguin, Inc.
Page 279: "Okay everybody, listen to this . . ." from *Near the Window Tree* by Karla Kuskin. Copyright © 1975 by Karla Kuskin. Reprinted by permission of Harper & Row, Publishers, Inc.
Page 280: Judith Viorst, "Good-Bye, Six-Hello, Seven" from *If I Were in Charge of the World and Other Worries*. Copyright © 1981 by Judith Viorst. Reprinted with the permission of Atheneum Publishers, Inc. and Lescher & Lescher, Ltd.
Page 281: From *Eliza's Daddy*, copyright © 1976 by Ianthe Thomas. Reprinted by permission of Harcourt Brace Jovanovich, Inc.
Page 299: Adaptation of complete text and specified illustrations from *Chameleon Was a Spy* by Diane Redfield Massie (Thomas Y. Crowell). Copyright © 1979 by Diane Redfield Massie. Reprinted by permission of Harper & Row, Publishers, Inc. and Janet A. Loranger, Literary Agent.
Page 326: Map from inside front cover from *The World of Pooh* by A. A. Milne, illustrated by E. H. Shepard. Copyright © 1957 by E.P. Dutton, renewed 1985 by E.P. Dutton. Reprinted by permission of E.P. Dutton, a division of New American Library and Curtis Brown Ltd., London.
Page 327: "Pooh Gets Into a Tight Place" (text and illustrations) from *Winnie-the-Pooh* by A. A. Milne, illustrated by E. H. Shepard. Copyright 1926 by E.P. Dutton, renewed 1954 by A. A. Milne. Line illustrations by E. H. Shepard copyright under the Berne Convention. Reprinted by permission of the publisher, E.P. Dutton, a division of New American Library, McClelland and Stewart Ltd., Methuen Children's Books and Curtis Brown, London.
Page 342: "The King's Breakfast" from *When We Were Very Young* by A. A. Milne, illustrated by E. H. Shepard. Copyright 1924 by E.P. Dutton, renewed 1952 by A. A. Milne. Reprinted by permission of the publisher, E.P. Dutton, a division of New American Library, McClelland and Stewart Ltd. and Methuen Children's Books.

ISBN 0-673-74407-8

Copyright © 1989, 1987,
Scott, Foresman and Company, Glenview, Illinois.
All Rights Reserved. Printed in the United States of America.

This publication is protected by Copyright and permission should be obtained from the publisher prior to any prohibited reproduction, storage in a retrieval system, or transmission in any form or by any means, electronic, mechanical, photocopying, recording, or otherwise. For information regarding permission, write to: Scott, Foresman and Company, 1900 East Lake Avenue, Glenview, Illinios 60025

12345678910-RRW-9796959439291908988

## Artists

Section 1: Jan Brett, 59-63, 65-71; Nan Brooks, 58, 73, 74; Dick Martin, 27, 29, 30, 32, 34, 36-38, 40, 41; Michael Norman, 45-56; David Povilaitis, 24-25; John Sanford, 42-44

*Acknowlegments continued on page 390*

# Contents

## Section Three
## Looking Ahead:
## Making Your Mark!

**3**

# Mitchell Is Moving

by Marjorie Sharmat

    Mitchell ran through his house. "So long. So long, everything," he shouted. Then he ran next door to Margo's house.

  "I'm moving," he said.

  "Where?" asked Margo.

  "Two weeks away," said Mitchell.

  "Where is that?" asked Margo.

"It's wherever I will be after I walk for two weeks," said Mitchell. "I have lived in the same place for a long time. It is time for me to go someplace else."

"No!" said Margo. "You have only lived next door for fifty years."

"Sixty," said Mitchell.

"Fifty, sixty. What's the difference?" said Margo. "I want you to stay next door forever."

"I can't," said Mitchell. "I do not want to wake up in the same old bedroom and eat breakfast in the same old kitchen and brush my scales and clean my nails in the same old bathroom. Every room in my house is the same old room because I have been there too long."

"Well, maybe you are just tired of the same old friend," said Margo.

"Who is that?" asked Mitchell.

"Me," said Margo. "Maybe you look at me and think, 'Same Old Face.

Same Old Tail.

Same Old Scales.

Same Old Walk.

Same Old Talk.

Same Old Margo.'"

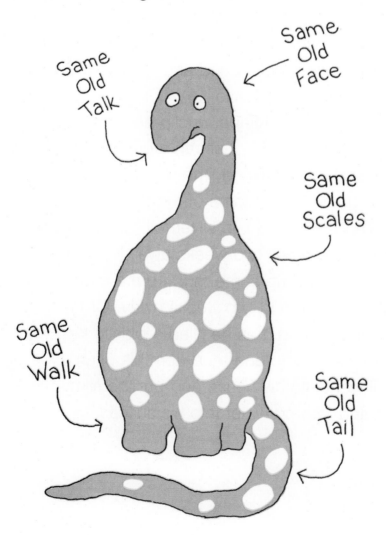

"No," said Mitchell. "I like your face, tail, scales, walk, and talk. I like you."

"I like, like, like you," said Margo.

"I like, like, like you, too," said Mitchell.

He walked to the door. "I must pack," he said.

Margo sat down in front of the door. "You can't get out," she said. "I will sit here for another sixty years."

"I still like you!" shouted Mitchell as he climbed out the window.

Margo called after him, "I will glue you to your roof. I will tie you to your front door with a thick green rope. I will tape you, paper-clip you to your house. Then I will get a gigantic rubber band and loop you to your house. I will not let you leave."

"I will unglue, untie, untape, unclip and unloop myself," said Mitchell. Mitchell ran around his house. "I'm moving, moving, moving," he shouted.

Then he gathered up some of the slimy moss near his house and wrapped it in silver foil. "Just in case there is no slimy moss two weeks away."

Mitchell scooped up some mud from a ditch. "Maybe there is no mud two weeks away. Or no swamp water," he said as he filled a plastic bag with water from his swamp and mud from his ditch.

Mitchell went into his house and put the slimy moss and mud and swamp water into his suitcase.

The telephone rang. Mitchell answered it.

"I will cement you to your ceiling," Margo said, and she hung up. "I am beginning to think that Margo does not want me to move," said Mitchell as he went back to his packing. He packed the cap and mitten set that Margo had given him. "Maybe it will be cold two weeks away," he thought.

Mitchell heard a shout. He went to his window. Margo was shouting, "I will take you to the laundromat in my laundry bag, and I will wash away your idea of moving."

"Margo is a good shouter," thought Mitchell.

He remembered when Margo had sent him a Happy Birthday Shout through the window:

"I'M GLAD YOU'RE THERE.

I'M GLAD I'M HERE.

HAPPY BIRTHDAY,

LOUD AND CLEAR."

"I wonder if there are any Happy Birthday Shouters two weeks away," thought Mitchell.

Mitchell held up the T-shirt that Margo had given him. It said:

MITCHELL, FRIEND OF MARGO

MARGO, FRIEND OF MITCHELL

"This shirt makes me feel sad that I am moving," said Mitchell. "But if I put it on I won't have to look at it."

Mitchell put on the T-shirt. "If I don't look down at my chest, I will feel all right."

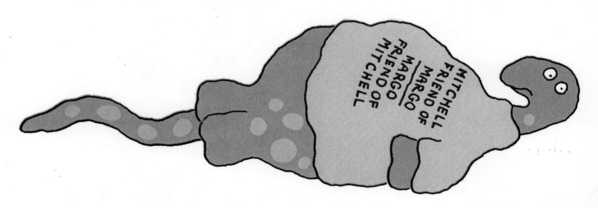

He closed his suitcase.

"There. I am all packed. I am ready to go."

Mitchell walked through his house.

"So long, same old rooms," he said. Mitchell took his suitcase and went to Margo's house.

"I am all ready to move," he said.

"I will stick you to your house with chewing gum," said Margo.

Mitchell picked up his suitcase and ran.

"Good-by!" he called. "I will write to you every day."

Mitchell stopped running and started to walk fast. "I am a moving Mitchell," he said.

Mitchell walked and walked.

When night came, he sent Margo a post card that said, "Dear Margo,

    Greetings from one day away."

The second night he wrote,
"Dear Margo,

    More greetings from two days away."

The third night he wrote,
"Dear Margo,

    More and more greetings from three days away."

"I am not much of a post-card writer," thought Mitchell. But he sent more and more greetings to Margo each night.

At last Mitchell reached two weeks away.

"I made it," he said.

Mitchell built a house and moved in.

"I will go to bed right away so I can wake up in my new bedroom," he said. "Mmm. New sleeps better," Mitchell said the next day. "Now I will eat my first meal in my new kitchen. Mmm. New tastes better."

Mitchell went outside and sat down in front of his house.

"This is a good house," he said. "But there is something missing. There is nobody next door. What good is a good house when there is nobody next door to it? I am lonely. I miss Margo."

Mitchell wrote a post card to Margo:

"Dear Margo,
   The most greetings ever from two weeks away.
The slimy moss is nice and slimy. The mud is nice
and thick. The swamp water is nice and mucky. But
I miss you. Please come to see me."

   Mitchell waited and waited. And waited.
   One morning he woke up and saw a bottle of glue,
a thick green rope, a big roll of tape, a huge paper
clip, a gigantic rubber band, a laundry bag, a sack of
cement and a package of chewing gum. Then he saw
Margo.
   "Mitchell!" said Margo.
   "Margo!" said Mitchell. "I am so happy to see you.
Here is my new house and my new everything."
   Mitchell showed Margo his new house and
everything around it.

"Two weeks away is terrific," said Margo as she and Mitchell ate breakfast.

"No, it isn't," said Mitchell. "There is nobody next door."

"Oh," said Margo. "I have the same problem where I am. There is nobody next door."

"I have an idea," said Mitchell, and he got some twigs and mud.

"I have the same idea," said Margo, and she filled her laundry bag with more twigs and mud. Then she got her bottle of glue, thick green rope, big roll of tape, huge paper clip, gigantic rubber band and sack of cement. "We can use these too," she said.

Mitchell and Margo built a house next door to Mitchell's house.

"Do you like it?" asked Mitchell.

"It's perfect," said Margo.

Margo moved into her new house. She shouted,

"I'VE COME TO STAY

TWO WEEKS AWAY.

HAPPY BIRTHDAY."

It wasn't Mitchell's birthday. But he was happy anyway.

# 1

# Learning About Me

Some days I look great—
some days I look awful.
Some days I know I am almost
perfect . . .
It's funny! On the days I am
almost perfect, my friends are
almost perfect too!

In this section you'll read
about some characters who
change, some who accept the way
they are, and some who learn to
see themselves in a new way.

# Understanding Character and Setting

Pretend you are lost at the zoo during a class trip. After you are found, you decide to write a story about how you felt, what you saw, and what you did. You are the **character** in the story you write.

When you want to find **characters** in a story you are reading, ask yourself, "Whom is this story about?" Each character will say, think, and do things that will help you understand what that character is like.

The **setting** is where and when the story takes place. In the story about getting lost during a class trip, the **setting** is a zoo. As you read, find words that make a picture of the place in your mind. Understanding the characters and the setting will help you understand the story better.

In the paragraph below, think about words that tell what the character Betty is like. Also, look for words that help you picture the setting.

Betty was resting on the sand, listening to the sound of the waves. Suddenly she remembered that she had to get a gift for her friend Carol. She had no money, so she thought and thought. Then she went looking for seashells. She washed them, put a hole in each, and tied them together on a string. Betty smiled. Now she had a gift for Carol.

1. What was Betty like? How do you know?

Did you say that Betty was a good friend? Or, did you think Betty was clever? She showed that she was both thoughtful and clever by what she did.

2. What is the setting of the story? How do you know?

Did you think that the beach was the setting? The words *sand*, *waves*, and *seashells* all tell you that Betty is at the beach.

3. How did Betty feel when she had finished Carol's gift? How do you know?

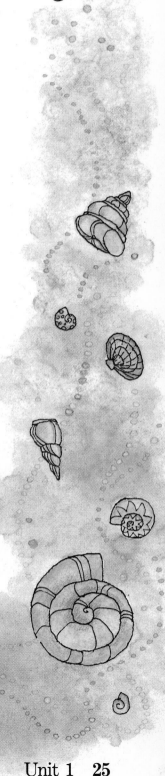

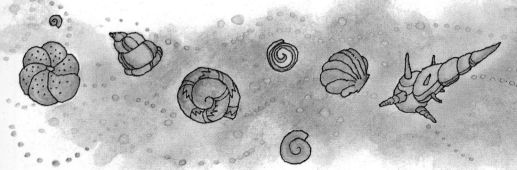

## Practicing Understanding Character and Setting
Read about Pete. Then answer the questions.

Pete was proud that his mom let him do the food shopping alone. He had almost everything he needed in his cart, but he was not quite tall enough to reach a can of peas. Pete moved a box over to the high shelf, but the box turned over and all the cans rolled out.

Pete felt awful. He wanted to run away. Then he decided to get to work. He picked up all the cans and put them back.

Mrs. Lee, the store owner, came over just before Pete was finished. Pete said he was sorry. He would put all the cans back.

Mrs. Lee wasn't angry. She thanked Pete for staying to help.

1. What do you think Pete is like?
2. How do you know?
3. What words tell you about the setting?

### Tips for Reading on Your Own
- Ask yourself who the story is about and what those characters say, think, do, and feel.
- Picture where the story takes place by finding words that tell about the setting.

*Geraldine wants to be good at something. As you read this story, ask yourself what important lesson Geraldine learns about herself. Notice what she says, thinks, and does to help you understand what she is like.*

# Just the Thing for Geraldine

by Ellen Conford

There was nothing Geraldine liked better than hanging by her tail from the branch of a tree and juggling a few acorns.

But her parents told her there was more to life than juggling, so every week she went to Mademoiselle La Fay's School of the Dance to learn ballet.

"It will help you to be graceful," said her mother.

"It will help you to be ladylike," said her father.

"It will help you keep physically fit," said her brother Randolph.

"Nothing could help her," whispered her brother Eugene.

One day Geraldine came home from ballet school very excited.

"Everybody come look!" she shouted. "Come look at what I can do!"

"What is it?" asked her mother.

"We learned the Dance of the Purple Swan," Geraldine said.

"That's wonderful!" said her mother.

"A whole dance!" exclaimed her father. "And you haven't even been going to dancing school very long."

"Swans aren't purple," said Eugene.

"Now, watch me," Geraldine ordered. "Are you looking?"

"We're looking," said her mother.

Geraldine smoothed down her tutu, which her mother had made for her out of leaves, and gracefully raised her forepaws over her head.

"Dee, da da da da dee ta dum," she hummed, and ran lightly, on tiptoe, around the trunk of the tree.

"Oh, how beautiful," sighed her mother.

"Encore, encore!" clapped her father.

"That's pretty good, Geraldine," said Randolph.

"Can we go play now?" asked Eugene.

"Dee, da da da da ta dum," Geraldine hummed, and began to dance faster around the tree.

But one of the big roots of the tree was sticking up from the ground and Geraldine didn't see it.

"Ow!" yelled Geraldine, as she tripped over the root and sprawled on the ground.

"Did you hurt yourself?" asked her mother worriedly.

"No," Geraldine sniffled, and ran up the tree before Randolph and Eugene could see her tears. She hung upside down by her tail, her leafy ballet skirt covering her face.

"I see you, Randolph," she said angrily. "You think I can't see you, but I can. You'd better stop laughing."

Randolph covered his mouth with his paw.

"I'm not laughing," he said, trying to sound serious.

"Is it all right if *I* laugh?" asked Eugene.

"There is nothing to laugh at," their father said sternly.

"Geraldine just tripped," their mother said. "It could happen to anybody."

"Especially Geraldine," whispered Eugene to Randolph.

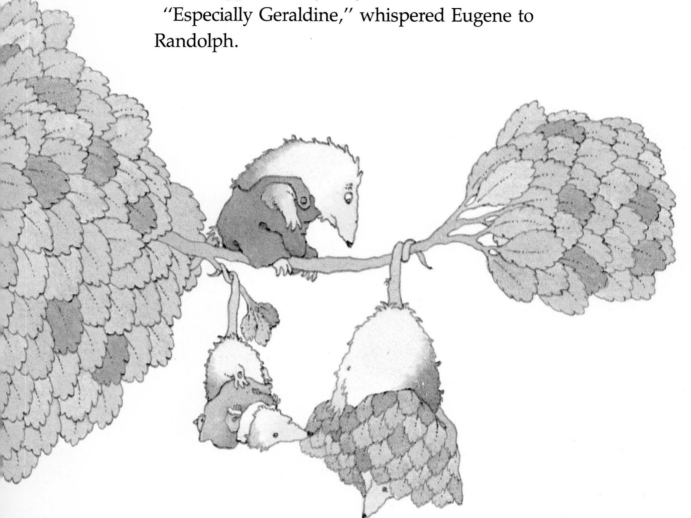

"I heard you, Eugene!" Geraldine shouted. "You think I can't hear you, but I can!" She pulled herself back up on the branch and straightened her tutu. "I'd like to see *you* do the Dance of the Purple Swan."

"Swans aren't purple," said Eugene. "Swans are white."

Randolph and Eugene went back to their game. Geraldine took off her ballet skirt. She looked at it thoughtfully as she folded it and put it away.

The following week, when Geraldine came home from ballet school, her mother and father were waiting for her.

"Well, what did you learn at dancing school today?" her mother asked eagerly.

"I learned," said Geraldine unhappily, "that I am not a very good dancer."

"Nonsense!" said her father. "You dance beautifully. And you haven't even been going to dancing school very long."

"And I don't think I'll be going much longer," said Geraldine.

"Oh, of course you will," said her mother. "You'll see, you'll be a graceful dancer in no time." Geraldine shook her head.

"No I won't," she said. "I cannot do pliés and arabesques, and when we're supposed to dance on our toes my toes curl up and I fall down. I am just not cut out for ballet."

"But I thought you liked ballet school," said her mother.

"I like juggling better," said Geraldine.

"But don't you want to learn to be graceful?" asked her father.

"No," said Geraldine, swinging back and forth by her tail from the branch of the tree and juggling some pebbles. "Not really."

"Oh," said her mother.

So, her mother signed her up for a class at Schuyler's School of Sculpture.

"I'm sure you have artistic talent," said her mother.

"Sculpture school is just the thing for you, Geraldine," agreed her father.

"I don't know," said Geraldine doubtfully, as she flipped three blackberries in the air and balanced a twig on the end of her nose.

"Oh, you'll see," said her mother. "You'll make bowls and pitchers and artistic statues. Sculpture school will be lots of fun."

Every week Geraldine went to Schuyler's School of Sculpture, and every week her parents asked, "How do you like sculpture school?"

And every week Geraldine shrugged and said, "It's okay, I guess."

One day Geraldine came home from class carrying a big pile of something wrapped in wet leaves.

"What's that?" asked Randolph.

"That's clay," said Geraldine.

"What's it for?" asked Eugene curiously.

"We have to make a sculpture of someone," Geraldine said.

"Oh, boy!" cried Eugene, jumping up and standing very straight and flexing his muscles. "Do me, Geraldine, do me!"

"We just have to do the head," Geraldine said.

"Oh," said Eugene, disappointed. "Well," he brightened a minute later, "do *my* head." He turned his head sideways so Geraldine could see his profile. "I have a nice head. Please, Geraldine?"

"You have to sit very still," Geraldine warned. "You can't move around or wiggle or anything."

"I won't," promised Eugene. "I won't even blink."

Geraldine sat Eugene down in front of her and turned his head sideways. She unwrapped the mound of clay and put it on a tree stump. Randolph sat down next to her.

"Don't sit there and watch me!" Geraldine snapped. "How do you expect me to concentrate when you're staring at me like that?"

"You're very touchy," said Randolph. "Why are you in such a bad mood?"

"I'm not in a bad mood!" yelled Geraldine. "Now, go away and leave me alone!"

Randolph went off to play ball and Geraldine began to work on her sculpture.

After a while, Eugene began to squirm.

"Is it finished yet, Geraldine?" he asked.

"No," said Geraldine.

"My nose itches," complained Eugene.

"Sit still and be quiet!" Geraldine ordered.

Geraldine molded the clay, squeezing it, poking it, and muttering to herself while she worked.

"What are you saying, Geraldine?" Eugene asked. "I can't hear you."

"I'm saying 'stupid clay!'" Geraldine snapped. "Now will you be still? How can I sculpt you if you keep wriggling around?"

"I can't help it," Eugene whined. "I'm getting tired. My neck hurts. And I think I have to sneeze."

"Be quiet. And I'm doing your mouth now, so please keep it shut."

Eugene sighed. Geraldine went on molding and muttering.

Finally she said, "There. It's done. I think."

"Oh, good!" said Eugene, jumping up and stretching. "I feel stiff all over. Let's see it."

But Geraldine was covering her sculpture with the wet leaves.

"Let me see it," Eugene said. "Why are you covering it up? I want to see my head."

He ran over to the tree stump and began pulling off the leaves.

"Stop it!" yelled Geraldine, swatting at him. "You stop that, Eugene! I don't want you to look at it. I don't want *anybody* to look at it."

"I won't hurt it," Eugene said, yanking off the leaves. "I want to see it."

Randolph and their mother and father came
running when they heard Eugene and Geraldine.

"What's going on?" asked their father.

"Why are you two screaming like this?" asked
their mother.

"*What* is *that?*" Randolph asked, pointing toward
the tree stump.

Eugene had pulled all the leaves off Geraldine's
sculpture and was backing away from the tree
stump, shaking his head in fury.

"That is *not me!*" he howled. "I don't look like that!"

"Well, if you didn't move around so much—"
Geraldine shouted.

"Is *that* supposed to be *Eugene?*" Randolph asked.

"It's . . . it's very interesting," their father said weakly.

"It is not interesting!" shrieked Eugene. "It's a bunch
of lumps! I don't look like a bunch of lumps!"

Geraldine sighed, and began to cover up her sculpture with leaves again. When she finished covering it all up, she climbed the tree and hung by her tail, swinging gently back and forth as she juggled some pine cones.

A little while later Randolph and Eugene came up the tree and sat down next to Geraldine.

"You sure are a good juggler, Geraldine," said Randolph kindly.

"Thank you," Geraldine murmured.

Randolph gave Eugene a poke in the ribs.

"Ow! I mean, oh," said Eugene, "I wish I could juggle like you can."

"Do you really?" Geraldine asked.

"You're the best juggler we know. ISN'T THAT
RIGHT, EUGENE?" said Randolph, glaring at his
brother.

"Yes," Eugene said.

"So we'd like you to teach us how to juggle,"
Randolph said. "WOULDN'T WE, EUGENE?"

"Yes," Eugene said.

"Oh," said Geraldine, happily, "of course I'll teach
you. It's not too hard, once you get the hang of it.
Now, just watch me and—"

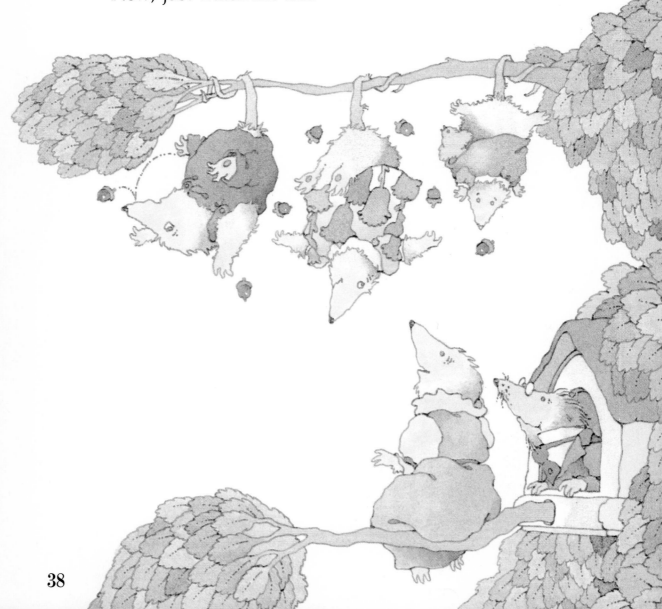

"Geraldine!" her mother called. "I've thought of just the thing for you!"

"What is it?" asked Geraldine.

"Singing lessons!" her mother said excitedly. "How would you like to take singing lessons?"

"No," said Geraldine, juggling her acorns.

"No?" her father asked. "But you'd love singing lessons."

"No," repeated Geraldine. "I wouldn't."

"But, why not, Geraldine?" asked her mother.

"What if I'm not a good singer?" said Geraldine. "I took ballet lessons and found out I wasn't a good dancer."

"And you certainly aren't good at sculpting," Eugene added.

"She sure is a good juggler, though," said Randolph. "And nobody ever gave her juggling lessons."

"That's true," their mother said.

"I never thought of that," said their father.

"Neither did I," said Geraldine.

Suddenly, she stopped juggling and jumped up. "I'll be right back," she said, and ran down the tree.

In a little while Geraldine returned. She was lugging a big piece of wood.

"What's that?" asked Randolph.

Geraldine propped the wood up against the trunk of the tree. "Come and look," she said proudly.

The possums came down from the tree.

"I made a sign," said Geraldine.

"What kind of a sign?" asked Eugene. "What does it say?"

"Oh, it's beautiful," said their mother.

"Aren't you the clever one!" said their father.

"What does it *say?*" cried Eugene. "Tell me what it says!"

"It says," Randolph told him, "Geraldine's Juggling School."

## Meet the Author

Like Geraldine, Ellen Conford learned she had a special skill. When she was in the third grade her teacher asked her to read the paper she had written in front of the class. Conford says, "I knew I had done *something* good. From that time on, I wrote."

Besides *Just the Thing for Geraldine*, Conford has written *And This Is Laura*, *Impossible Possum*, and *Why Can't I Be William?*

# Comprehension Check

*Think and Discuss*

*See your Thinker's Handbook for tips.*

- 1. What important lesson does Geraldine learn about herself in this story?
- 2. What does Geraldine most like to do?
- 3. Why do Geraldine's parents want her to learn ballet?
- 4. How does Geraldine feel after she dances for her family? How do you know?
- 5. Is Randolph a good brother to Geraldine? Why?

● Literary Skill: Character

# Communication Workshop

*Talk*

Do you have a special skill such as juggling or dancing? Talk with a partner about each other's skills. Make a list of two or three skills and then decide which skill you would like to share with the class.

Speaking/Listening: Discussion

*Write*

Pretend that you have decided to open a school where you teach other people your special skill. Make a sign for your school, then write two sentences telling what you will teach there. Share your sign and sentences with your class.

Writing Fluency: Sentences

*Many people think about being something they are not. Some wish for things that can never be. Think about what the donkey in this story wants and if he gets what he wants.*

# The Donkey in the Lion's Skin

by Nancy Ross Ryan

Once there lived a donkey who wished to be a lion. Every time he heard a lion roar he was sad.

"If only I could roar like a lion," he said. "Instead, I can only bray."

Each day when the sun came up, he woke the cat.

"What is that awful noise?" asked the cat.

"I am roaring," the donkey said.

"No, you are braying," complained the cat. "Please stop and let me sleep."

At noon, he frightened the mouse.

"My, oh my!" said the mouse. "What is that awful noise?"

"I am roaring," the donkey said.

"You are braying, silly donkey," said the mouse. "Now please stop so my children can take a nap."

In the middle of the night, the donkey surprised the owl.

"What is that awful noise?" hooted the owl.

"I am roaring," the donkey said.

"Lions roar, but donkeys bray," hooted the owl.

Soon, all the animals complained about the noisy donkey.

"Why can't he stop trying to be a lion? We can't sleep anymore because of his silly noise."

One day, the donkey bought a lion's skin. He threw the lion's skin over his head.

"At last, the animals will think I am a lion," he said.

Dressed in the lion's skin, the donkey met the cat. He jumped in front of the cat and roared. Instead of running away, the little cat laughed.

Next, the donkey met the mouse. He shook the lion's skin and roared. Instead of jumping, the little mouse laughed.

That night, the donkey dressed in the lion's skin again. He went to the owl's tree and roared. The owl just laughed instead of being surprised.

"You may try to look like a lion. But you still sound like a donkey. Go home and be what you are."

*Be the best of what you are. That is the best you can be.*

*This selection tells of a family who lived 200 years ago. Can you imagine moving to a new land where there are no towns or cities? Felipe does just that. As you read, think about what Felipe and his family want and if they get what they want. How do they see Felipe in a whole new way?*

# How Far, Felipe?

by Genevieve Gray

Felipe lived with Uncle Carlos, Aunt Maria, and his six cousins. His friend was Filomena, a baby burro. Filomena was very loud but very small—too small to help on the farm. Uncle Carlos tried to grow corn but the land was poor. Felipe was often hungry. So were his cousins. So were most people in their town in Mexico.

One day in the plaza Felipe and Filomena saw an
officer talking to the crowd. "I am Colonel Anza,"
he said. "The Viceroy of Mexico needs thirty
families to settle in California. Land is rich there. It
is good for farms and ranches. Each family will get
clothes, food, horses, and ranch animals. All free.
California is four months away by horseback. My
soldiers and I will take you there. Who will go?"

"Food? Clothes?" Felipe whispered to Filomena.
Then he shouted, "I will go!"

Others began to shout, "We will go to
California!"

Filomena cried, "EEEEEAW–ee–AW!" She was so loud that horses reared and pigs squealed.

"Get that burro out of here!" cried Colonel Anza.

Felipe ran to tell Uncle Carlos. But Uncle Carlos said, "California is too far away."

"Who cares?" said Aunt Maria. "We live like toads here! We need the food and clothes."

They went to sign up.

"I will take Filomena to California," Felipe said.

"No!" said Uncle Carlos, "she is too small to work."

"When will she be big enough?" asked Felipe.

"When her shoulder is as tall as you," said Uncle Carlos. "But by then you will be in California."

"EEEEEAW—ee—AW!" sang Filomena.

Only Felipe understood. Filomena was going to California, too.

"We will cross deserts and mountains," said Colonel Anza. "We will meet friendly Indians and some that are not so friendly. It will be a hard journey."

At last everything was ready. Colonel Anza led the caravan. Behind him rode soldiers. Then came the families. Then more soldiers. Then the pack mules and the cattle. At the end came Filomena.

Felipe rode on a horse. So did his cousins José and Ruben. He looked and looked for Filomena. Then he heard her calling him. EEEEEAW—ee—AW!" The horses jerked the reins. The mules threw off their loads. Cattle ran into the bushes. The caravan stopped.

"Get rid of that burro!" shouted Colonel Anza. But no one heard him. The soldiers were too busy catching animals.

Late that afternoon, Colonel Anza stopped beside a stream. "We will camp here for the night," he said.

Men unloaded the mules and put up the tents. Women built cooking fires and started supper. Children played in the woods. Felipe found Filomena eating grass with the mules.

"I love you, Filomena," whispered Felipe. She put her head against his chest.

The next morning a soldier blew a horn for time-to-get-up. Filomena sang along, "EEEEEAW–ee–AW–ee–AW!" Everybody got up very fast. Colonel Anza laughed.

"This burro is not so bad," he said.

After that, Filomena sang "time-to-get-up" every morning. Felipe was proud. Even Uncle Carlos looked a little pleased.

A few days later they came to a mountain pass. Rocks rose high all around. Colonel Anza was afraid of an Indian attack. "Apache scouts will be watching from those rocks," he said.

They went through the narrow pass. They climbed through a canyon. They crept along a ledge. No one slept that night. All night, Felipe listened for Apaches. He thought he saw some scouts, but they were only shadows.

The caravan moved out at dawn. Nobody ate breakfast. "By noon, we will be safe," said Colonel Anza. "Then we will eat."

"California better be good!" grumbled Aunt Maria.

"If we ever get there," said Uncle Carlos.

They came to a desert. They rode for weeks
through miles and miles and miles of desert.

"We left home last summer," said Felipe.

"Now it is nearly winter, and no California!"

"We are halfway there," said Colonel Anza. "San
Gabriel is only two months away."

Everyone was too tired to care. "Two months,
two years, it's all the same," grumbled Aunt Maria.

They came to a river. Indians lived along the
bank. "These are Pima Indians," said Colonel Anza.
'They are friendly."

The Indians brought food. When Aunt Maria gave them chocolate to drink, they made faces and spit it out.

"The Apaches were better," said Aunt Maria.

The caravan stayed there for three days. Felipe filled water kegs and helped with the animals. Uncle Carlos was surprised. "Is Felipe a cowboy now?" he said to Aunt Maria. "What next?"

One day the Indians gave a feast. Felipe ate lots of beans and corn. One man helped him cut some watermelon for Filomena. But she did not like watermelon. So Felipe ate her piece.

The caravan moved on through the desert. Cold winds blew sand and dust. Now there was almost no water. There was no grass for the animals. Only Filomena found a few weeds to eat. It was so cold that Felipe and Filomena slept together to keep warm. The other animals stood all night, hungry and cold, with their backs to the wind.

One morning, Felipe saw nine mules dead. Colonel Anza said sadly, "No food, no water. It is a miracle that any are alive."

"If animals die, people may die," said Uncle Carlos.

Felipe walked beside his tired horse. The cold wind whipped his face. He saw starving animals fall and die.

That night, Uncle Carlos said, "We must dig holes in the dry river to get water for the animals."

Felipe told Filomena, "I must help the men tonight, but you will stay warm."

He asked his cousins, "Who wants to sleep with Filomena?"

"I do!" they all cried.

Felipe worked all night digging holes for water. He brought animals to drink one by one. He forgot how cold and tired he was. But when dawn came, 96 more animals were dead. The caravan had to move on.

Felipe saw something strange. "What is that white stuff?" he asked.

"Snow," said Colonel Anza. "You never saw snow where you lived in Mexico."

That night, they sat around tiny campfires wrapped in blankets. But they were still cold.

Next morning, the sky was clear. Felipe saw far mountains all white with snow. "California is nothing but ice and snow!" cried Uncle Carlos. "At home, we were poor but at least we were warm!"

"You want to go back?" asked Aunt Maria.

But the sun felt warm on Felipe's shoulders.

"Look!" cried cousin Ruben, "the snow is melting a little!"

"EEEEEAW–ee–AW!" cried Filomena.

The mountains were just ahead. She smelled water bubbling from the mountain springs. She smelled winter grass growing in the valleys. The horses walked faster.

That afternoon, they came to the start of the mountains. There was water for everyone. And rich grass for the animals. "We made it!" shouted Felipe.

Felipe helped unload the tired animals and lead them to the grass.

"That was the hard part," cried Colonel Anza. "The rest will be easy."

"God be thanked," said Aunt Maria.

They rested for a week. Then they climbed into the mountains. Tall trees and green grass grew everywhere. Felipe found sunflowers and wild grapes. The sun was bright on the river. There was plenty of fish.

"But where is California?" Felipe asked.

"This *is* California!" said Colonel Anza. "We are almost at San Gabriel."

"Look at Filomena," cried Ruben. "She has grown!"

"Her shoulder is as tall as Felipe now!" said Aunt Maria.

"EEEEEAW—ee—AW!" sang Filomena proudly. She let Felipe climb on her back. Her muscles were strong. She trotted in a little circle, showing off.

"Our cowboy has a horse!" cried Uncle Carlos.

"She will pull logs when we build our new house!" cried Ruben.

"And plow!" cried Uncle Carlos.

"Easy there!" said Aunt Maria. "Don't work our little friend too hard!" She rubbed Filomena's nose. At last they came through the mountains. They saw green hills rolling away to the sea. The fathers of the Mission of San Gabriel came to meet them.

"We are home at last," Felipe whispered to Filomena.

And Filomena sang, "EEEEEAW—ee—AW—ee—AW!"

# Comprehension Check

*Think and Discuss*

• **1.** What does the donkey in the first selection want?

• **2.** What things does the donkey try in order to get what he wants?

**3.** What does the donkey in *The Donkey in the Lion's Skin* learn about himself?

• **4.** Why does Felipe's family go to California?

**5.** What are some of the problems the family has in getting to California?

● Literary Skill: Goal and outcome

# Communication Workshop

*Talk*

Work with a group of your classmates to brainstorm for ideas on how Felipe's journey to California is different from a trip you might make today. Write down as many differences as possible.

Speaking/Listening: Group discussion

*Write*

Imagine you and your family are going to California by car. Choose four differences from the group list. Then write four sentences telling how your trip today would be different from the one Felipe made. Share your sentences with your group.

Writing Fluency: Sentences

# Watching for Special Type

Look at Molly. Did she speak to her baby brother in a soft, sweet voice? **NO!** What gave you a clue about how she sounded? It's the type! The dark type shows you that Molly was talking in a big, loud voice.

You read different kinds of type every day. Type that is different catches your eye. It makes you look at it. Think of how many different kinds of type you see in school.

When you read a play, the name of the character who is speaking is printed in small capital letters.

MIKE: I'm going now!

DAD: Okay, Mike. See you later.

If you are reading your social studies book, you might find a new word in darker type like this: **new word.**

Look at the paragraph at the top of the next **selection.** *The type is like this.* That's so you know it's *about* the play and not *part of it.*

Start being a type watcher. It's fun!

*Sometimes characters in stories think they can get anything they want because they are big and strong. As you read this play, ask yourself if even great kings might ever need someone's help. At the end of Act 1, see if you can tell what will happen next to Tiger and Ant.*

# The Two Kings
(a play based on an old Indian tale)
by Charnan Simon

### CHARACTERS

| | | | |
|---|---|---|---|
| ANT | BIRDS | ELEPHANT | HYENA |
| TIGER | MONKEYS | DEER | |

## ACT 1

*(Act 1 takes place in the jungle.)*

**BIRDS:** We are the birds, the birds of the jungle.
What will we see from our treetop today?

**BIRD #1:** Look! There is Tiger, King of the Jungle!
He's huge and he's hungry, and he is also
dreaded by all.

**BIRD #2:** But now he's asleep.

**BIRDS:** Shh! Do not wake him.
It's day and not night,
But he will be mad
If we wake him all right!

(BIRDS *fly away as* ANT *walks in.*)

60

**ANT:** Well, well, well, who have we here? Neighbor Tiger is taking a nap right across my path. I'll have to climb over him.

**TIGER:** Ha! What have I caught walking across my nose? How *dare* you wake me, Ant? Don't you know I am King of the Jungle? Look how much bigger and stronger I am than you. Why, I could crush you between my teeth!

**ANT:** Pardon me. It is true that your teeth are big and sharp, while I am tiny. However, I am also a king. One king should not crush another.

**TIGER:** How can you be a king? You are too small.

**ANT:** The best kings are not always the biggest, cousin. I am King of the Ants.

**TIGER:** If you are really a king, show me by answering these riddles.

(MONKEYS *come in in a noisy group.*)

**MONKEYS:** We heard that! Riddles—we love riddles!
   Listen to this one.

**MONKEY #1:** What did one eye say to the other eye?

**MONKEYS:** There is something between us that
   smells! *(All laugh.)*

**TIGER:** Silence! This is not a game!

**MONKEY #2:** Right, chief. But how about this one?
   What is the one question you can't answer
   *yes* to?

**MONKEYS:** Are you asleep? *(All laugh.)*

**TIGER:** Enough! Be gone! Stay out of my royal sight.
   Obey me, or I will make monkey meat
   out of you!

*(*MONKEYS *leave.)*

**TIGER:** Now, Ant, answer me this. What has a bed but never rests?

**ANT:** A good question. The answer flows all through the jungle. It is the river.

**TIGER:** You please me, Ant. Think of this river as you solve my second riddle. What can go through water but never gets wet?

**ANT:** It is the sunlight that shines even as we stand here.

**TIGER:** Fast thinking, friend Ant! Now, answer my third and last riddle, and you will go free. What flies faster than the wind?

**ANT:** That can only be Time, which will age us all, great and small.

**TIGER:** Spoken like a true king! You may go free, Ant. But remember, I, King of the Jungle, have let you go free.

**ANT:** And I hope to help *you* sometime.

**TIGER:** Ha, ha! Well, you are too small for that, but thank you for the offer.

**ANT:** Do not be so sure I'm too small to ever help you. Our paths may cross on another day, and it is hard to know who will help the other then.

**TIGER:** Well, be that as it may, be off now and let me finish my nap.

● What do you think will happen next?

## ACT 2

*(Act 2 takes place at the door of* TIGER'S *cave. The roof has crashed down inside the cave.)*

**BIRDS:** Here we are, the birds of the jungle.
But what do we see from our treetop today?
It is Tiger, our king,
And he's in a royal mess!
The roof of his cave
Has crashed down upon him.
We must surely call for help
If we want to save him!
Elephant! Deer! Hyena! Come quick!
Even these monkeys just might do
the trick!

*(*ELEPHANT, DEER, HYENA, *and* MONKEYS *come in.)*

**ELEPHANT:** It is I, mighty Elephant, the largest animal in the jungle. However, my great size is of no use to me now. I am too big to get into the cave to save our king.

**DEER:** I also would help if I could. I can run fast and jump far, but I cannot spare the time to clean away all that sand. I only have four hooves! Oh, King Tiger, are you all right in there?

**TIGER:** Go away, Deer! You are only good for eating!

**ELEPHANT:** Oh, proud Tiger, now is not the time to say such things. Deer only wanted to help. What about you, Hyena? Can you dig away the sand?

**HYENA:** Sorry, sorry, sorry! There is only one of me, and a whole hill of sand. I could never dig all that away. And Tiger might want to eat me, too, after being caught in that cave for such a long time. Surely you agree that he sounds both hungry *and* angry! What about those monkeys? There are so many of them.

**MONKEYS:** Never, never, never! King Tiger warned us to stay away from him. He will make monkey meat out of us if we get close. No, thank you! Instead we will stay up here in our tree, where it is safe.

**BIRDS:** And how could *we* help?
We are many, but small.
No, I fear we could not reach
King Tiger at all.
And then, it is true—
He might eat us, too!

**ELEPHANT:** I am sorry, King Tiger. Those of us who would help you cannot, and those who could help you will not. You have threatened the smaller animals of your kingdom with your sharp teeth and hungry ways, and we larger animals are too big to help. Now night is falling, and we must all return to our jungle homes. Maybe you'll get free on your own.

*(Animals all leave, but* BIRDS *stay.)*

**TIGER:** Now I am left alone, with no friend to save me. I am afraid it is the end for this tiger. I am the king, but even a king sometimes needs help.

(ANT KING *comes in with other ants.*)

**ANT:** Come, everybody, let's hurry! This whole hill of sand is huge, but each grain does not weigh much. If we spread out and each carry away one grain of sand, between all of us we will soon free Tiger. So let's move this hill!

**TIGER:** Is that you I hear, Ant? Can it be?

**ANT:** Yes, friend Tiger. I called thousands of my ants together just as soon as I heard the news. Remember, I owe you my life—now I can help save yours in return. Steady, now.

(*Ants clean away sand to free* TIGER.)

**TIGER:** Free at last! It was surely my good fortune the day I met you, Ant. I was wrong to make fun of you for being small. You were right when you said the best kings are not always the biggest. Of all these animals in the jungle, only you, the smallest of them all, were able to save me. I have learned my lesson. Tall or short, size does not matter to me anymore. I agree that you are a true king!

**ANT:** Come! Now that you are free, let us call together the other animals. It is time to celebrate as friends!

**THE END**

## Think and Discuss

- **1.** Were you right about what you said would happen with Tiger and Ant at the end of Act 1? What made you think as you did?
- **2.** What was Tiger's problem?
- **3.** What did you think of Tiger at the beginning of the play? and at the end?
- **4.** Why doesn't each of the following help Tiger: Elephant, Deer, Hyena, Monkeys, and Birds?
- **5.** What does Tiger learn about himself and others?

● Comprehension Skill: Predicting outcomes

## Communication Workshop

### Talk

Choose a partner and decide who should pretend to be Tiger and Ant. Work together to list what the characters say, think, and do that makes them kings. Then discuss which of the two kings is a better ruler. Why do you think so?

Speaking/Listening: Cooperative learning

### Write

Use your list to write three rules which show that your character is a better ruler. Read them to your class and have your partner read his or her rules. Who does the class think is the better ruler? Why?

Writing Fluency: Rules

# How to Tell a Tiger

by John Ciardi

People who know tigers
    Very very well
All agree that tigers
    Are not hard to tell.

The way to tell a tiger is
    With lots of room to spare.
Don't try telling them up close
    Or we may not find you there.

# There Was a Young Lady of Riga

anonymous

There was a young lady of Riga,
Who rode with a smile on a tiger,
They returned from the ride
With the lady inside,
And the smile on the face of the tiger.

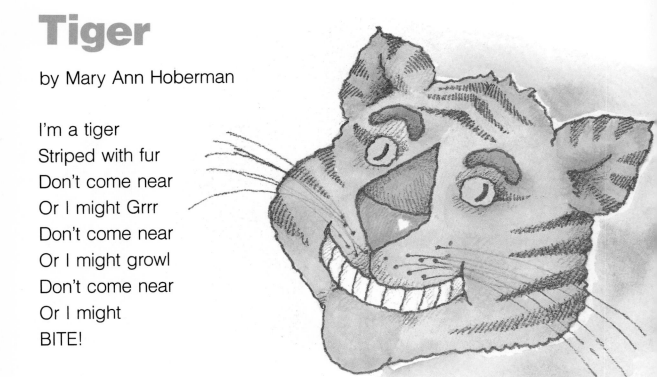

# Tiger

by Mary Ann Hoberman

I'm a tiger
Striped with fur
Don't come near
Or I might Grrr
Don't come near
Or I might growl
Don't come near
Or I might
BITE!

# LOOKING BACK

See your Thinker's Handbook for tips.

**Prewriting**

**Thinking and Writing About the Section**
In this section you read about characters who learn about themselves. You can write a narrative paragraph to tell one of their stories to another class. To begin, copy the chart and talk with a partner to fill it in.

| Who | Wants | Events | What happens |
|---|---|---|---|
| Geraldine | | | |
| Donkey | to be a lion | | |
| Felipe | | | |
| Tiger | | | learns kings need help |

**Writing**

Choose one of the characters in your chart and write a narrative paragraph to tell his or her story. Put the events in the order in which they happened. For more information on narrative paragraphs, see your Writer's Handbook.

**Revising**

Read your first draft to a partner. Are the events in order? Make changes and proofread. Write the final copy.

**Presenting**

Be a storyteller and share your paragraph with another class. What did they especially like?

# 2

# Cities Old and New

**The City**
In the morning the city
Spreads its wings
Making a song
In stone that sings.

by *Langston Hughes*

A city is a busy, noisy, living thing. A city saves its past by keeping old buildings. It reaches to the future with new buildings.

You will read about three cities that mix the old and the new. You'll also read about a town not found on any map.

# Making Comparisons

John's family will move from a big city to the country. John wants to know what kind of school he will go to. His dad showed him a picture of the new school. John made the chart you see below to compare the two schools.

| | Kind of Building | Size | Color |
|---|---|---|---|
| City | School | Large | Red |
| Country | School | One room | White |

John sees the buildings are alike because they are both schools. They are different in size and color.

When you find how things are alike and different, you are **comparing** them. When you read, you also need to understand how things are the same and how they're different. Sometimes writers make **comparisons** for you; sometimes you have to make them yourself using the information a writer gives you. Clue words such as these can help you:

same     both     but     different     like     unlike

Read about a city school and country school. Look for words that show how two things can be compared.

John goes to a city school which is a large building with many rooms. John has a different teacher for reading than he has for math. That is unlike the country school, where children from many grades will be in one room, and John will have only one teacher. Yet in both schools, John learns the same things in reading and math.

1. What is the same for John in both schools?

Did you say that John would still learn the same reading and math? Those things will be the same in both schools.

2. What clue words in the paragraph tell you two things are being compared?

The words *different, unlike, yet, both* and *same* are clue words showing comparison.

3. How will the size of the country school be different from that of the city school?
4. In what other ways are the two schools different?

## Practicing Making Comparisons

Read the next paragraph about Chicago and San Francisco and think of ways to compare them.

Chicago and San Francisco are both great cities. There are many things to see and do in each city. Chicago and San Francisco are different in some ways. Chicago is in the middle of the United States, but San Francisco is in the West. Chicago is a large city. In Chicago the weather changes from hot to cold, but San Francisco's weather stays cool all year. In Chicago the land is flat, unlike San Francisco which has many hills.

1. Name two ways in which San Francisco is like Chicago.
2. How is the weather in Chicago different from the weather in San Francisco?
3. Compare the land in San Francisco to the land in Chicago.

## Tips for Reading On Your Own

- Look to see if two things are being compared.
- Look for clue words such as *like, different, both,* and *unlike.*
- See if you can make a chart of the way things are alike and different.

*A city such as New York has many old homes among the new, tall buildings. In this story, Peter hates living in an old house. Read to find out what Peter learns about his old house. As you read, notice comparisons the characters make.*

# Peter's Brownstone House

by Hila Colman

Once, a long time ago, a beautiful house was built in New York City. It had a wide stoop and an iron railing with a gate in front.

Inside, the rooms were large, with high ceilings. Almost every one had a fireplace. Many of them had glittering lamps that were lighted with hundreds of tiny candles. The stairway, with its smooth, dark wood, was wide and graceful.

The people who built the house wanted it to last for many, many years. The house did last for many years, although it was slowly surrounded by tall buildings.

Even then people still lived in it: a boy named Peter and his great-grandfather, whom he called Grandpa.

Peter, however, hated the old house. He wanted to live in the tall, new apartment building across the way. His best friend John lived there. Then Peter could ride up and down in the elevator. He could say good morning to the jolly doorman.

But Grandpa loved his old, old house. He hated new apartment buildings. "Nothing is the way it used to be," he grumbled.

One day a man came to see Grandpa. He wanted to buy the old-fashioned brownstone. He offered a large sum of money for it.

"We want to tear it down," he said. "We'll put up a modern apartment house."

"Can we live in the new house when it is built?" asked Peter eagerly.

"Sure you can," the man said.

Peter was very excited. However, Grandpa said he had to think it over. He loved the old house.

Grandpa said, "I love it because it is old. I was born in this house. I don't like the idea of its being torn down. But I will think about it."

"Let's go for a walk," he said to Peter.

Everywhere they looked on the street old houses were being torn down. New houses were going up. Grandpa said with a sigh, "The city is not the way it used to be when I was a boy."

"What was it like then?" Peter asked.

Before Grandpa could answer, a loud siren made Peter and Grandpa jump. A huge fire engine came rushing around the corner with the firefighters hanging on to it. "Look at them go!" Peter cried. "Bet you didn't have anything like that!"

Grandpa said, "We didn't. Horses pulled the fire engines. They had bells that went ting-a-ling-a-ling. Sometimes there was a bucket brigade. That is a whole line of people passing a bucket from the well to the fire!"

"A well?" Peter was surprised.

"Yes, there were lots of wells. When I visited my grandfather, I would pump the water every morning to get washed. I'll show you where my grandfather's house was," said Grandpa.

Grandpa took Peter to a street between the park and the river. It was busy and noisy and lots of children were playing on the sidewalk. "See that drugstore on the corner," Grandpa said. "My grandfather's farmhouse used to be there. And where those children are roller skating is where I used to plant the corn. It was beautiful then."

They started to cross the street. The police officer blew her whistle. "Watch the lights," she called to them.

Grandpa took Peter by the hand. "My mind was way back in the past. It was quiet and peaceful here. You could hear the birds singing and the cows mooing."

"You had police officers, didn't you?" Peter asked.

"Yes," Grandpa nodded his head, "although they were different. They didn't have to stop traffic because there weren't any cars or trucks. The police rode on bicycles to keep an eye on things."

Peter and Grandpa agreed that it must have been fun.

Now they were facing the river. "Let's go down to see the boats," Peter said.

But they couldn't get near the river. Instead they saw huge buildings that Grandpa called docks behind high wire fences. Peter looked through the fence and watched a big crane lift a car from the deck of a ship onto the dock.

"I wish I could go down to the water," Peter complained.

"You could when I was a boy," Grandpa told him.

By now it was getting late. All at once the street lights came on. The city glowed with lights. "It was very different in my day," Grandpa said. "The gaslighter went from lamp to lamp. He lit each lamp one at a time. We didn't have electricity then."

Grandpa was tired, so they took a bus home. "In the old days, we would be riding in a horse-pulled car. I don't think it was any slower than a bus in all this traffic," he grumbled.

When they got home, Peter sat in his favorite window seat. He was looking longingly at the apartment house across the way. Lights were twinkling in every window. But suddenly, as he was looking at it, all the lights went out! The lights in the apartment house, the lights on the street, and the lights in his own house!

Grandpa called to him. "Peter, where are you? What happened?"

"I don't know," Peter called back.

Peter turned on his battery radio and a man's voice said, "The electricity is out all over the city. Most apartments will have no heat, no lights, and no working elevators."

"Well, we'll be all right," said Grandpa with a chuckle. "I'll find some candles. You build fires in the fireplaces. I think I can turn on the gas in the basement. Then we'll light the old gaslights on the wall."

Soon the fires were blazing. Grandpa was able to hook up the gas and light the old gaslights. He also put some silver candlesticks on the mantel.

Peter looked around the living room. He thought he had never seen anything so beautiful. The candlelight and the firelight gave the room a soft, cozy glow.

Then Peter thought of his friend John in the apartment house. "Grandpa," he cried. "I want to see if John is all right. Maybe he can't get home if the elevators are not working."

"Take the flashlight and go ask the doorman," Grandpa said.

Peter found John on the first floor of the tall building. He was trying to get up the courage to walk up sixteen flights of stairs. John knew it would be cold and dark when he got home.

"Come over to my house," Peter said. "We have lights and heat. And we don't need an elevator."

"Hurray!" John cried. The two boys ran back across the street.

They had never known before what fun an old house could be. They added logs to the fire. They ran up the stairs to Peter's big playroom. They talked to each other on the old-fashioned house phones from one floor to the next.

When it was time to eat, Grandpa made them a wonderful meal. He cooked on the old coal stove in the kitchen. They put food on the little kitchen elevator and pulled it upstairs. Then they could eat in front of the warm fire.

"I wish the electricity would never get fixed," said John. But just then the lights came on. Soon John left to go home.

The next day the man came back to ask Grandpa if he had decided to sell the house. "I'll ask my grandson," he told the man.

"Peter," Grandpa called to him, "come and tell the man if you want to sell the house."

"I should say not," cried Peter. "I wouldn't sell this house for a million dollars. There are hundreds of apartment houses, but there's only one house just like this in the whole city."

The man went away very disappointed.

Peter and Grandpa still live in their old brownstone house. Every time Peter passes the apartment house across the way, he waves to the jolly doorman. But he is glad that he lives in his big, old-fashioned brownstone.

# Comprehension Check

*Think and Discuss*

1. What does Peter learn that makes him feel different about his old house?
2. Where does Peter think he would like to live at first? Why does he want to live there?
3. Compare Grandpa's feeling about living in an apartment building with living in his own house.
4. Peter's city was different when Grandpa was a boy. Name three ways the city has changed.
5. Would you rather live in an old house or in a new apartment building? Tell why.

*See your Thinker's Handbook for tips.*

Comprehension Skill: Comparative relationships

# Communication Workshop

*Talk*

Choose a partner and imagine that you both live in apartments on the 50th floor of a building. Make a list of ways your life would change if the electricity went out all over your city.

Speaking/Listening: Cooperative learning

*Write*

A reporter wants to find out what happened during the black-out. Write three things about your life in the apartment or in an old-fashioned brownstone. Read your sentences to your partner.

Writing Fluency: Sentences

# Using a Dictionary or Glossary

The city of Boston is <u>famous</u> for old-fashioned baked beans.

You may not know the underlined word in the sentence above. It is hard to understand the sentence without knowing that word. Where can you go to find the meaning of a word?

A **dictionary** or a **glossary** is the place to go to find out more about words. A **dictionary** is a book of words and their meanings. A **glossary** is a short dictionary at the back of some books.

The words in both a dictionary and a glossary are in **alphabetical** order. That means they begin with words starting with the letter *a* and end with words starting with the letter *z*. To find the word *famous* in the dictionary, you would look in the *f*'s.

Should you read every page of words starting with *f* to find the word *famous?* No. **Guide words** will help you. **Guide words** are written in large, dark type at the top of each page. They show the first and last words on that page. For example, if the guide words on a page are *free* and *fuss*, you know that *famous* cannot be on that page because the letters f–a–m come before the letters f–r–e in the alphabet. Guide words can save you time.

The word you are looking for, such as *famous*, is called the **entry word.** The entry word and all the information about that word is called the **entry.** In the entry you will find the word divided into syllables, information on how to say the word, and the meaning of the word. Sometimes the entry word is used in a sentence. Some entry words have a picture. The sentence and the picture may help you with the meaning.

Look at the dictionary page printed on the next page. What guide words do you see?

Yes, the guide words are **fame** and **faraway.**

Do you know if you will find the word *famous* on this page without looking at the entry words?

*Famous* will be on this page because the letters f–a–m–o come between the two guide words.

Read the entry for **famous.**

**fame** (fām), having much said or written about one; being very well known: *the hero's fame.*

**famed** (fāmd), famous; well-known.

**fam·i·ly** (fam′ə lē), **1** father, mother, and their children: *Our town has about a thousand families.* **2** children of a father and mother; offspring: *They are raising a family.* **3** group of people living in the same house. **4** all of a person's relatives: *a family reunion.* **5** group of related animals or plants. Lions, tigers, and leopards belong to the cat family. *plural* **fam·i·lies.**

**fam·ine** (fam′ən), **1** lack of food in a place; a time of starving: *Many people died during the famine in India.* **2** starvation: *Many people died of famine.* **3** a very great lack of anything: *a coal famine.*

**fam·ish** (fam′ish), be very hungry; starve: *She was famished after not eating for ten hours.*

**fa·mous** (fā′məs), very well known; noted: *The famous singer was greeted by a large crowd.*

**fan** (fan), **1** instrument or device with which to stir the air in order to cool a room or one's face, or to blow dust away. **2** stir (the air); blow on; stir up: *Fan the fire to make it burn faster.* **3.** use a fan on: *She fanned herself.* **4** anything that is flat and spread out like an open fan: *The peacock spread out its tail into a beautiful fan.* **fanned, fan·ning.**

**fan·ci·ful** (fan′sə fəl), **1** showing fancy; quaint; odd; fantastic: *Fanciful decorations are made up, not patterned after something.* **2** led by fancy; using fancies: *Hans Christian Andersen was a fanciful writer.* **3** suggested by fancy; imaginary; unreal. See picture.

| | | | |
|---|---|---|---|
| **a** hat | **ī** ice | **ù** put | **ə** stands for: |
| **ā** age | **o** hot | **ü** rule | a in about |
| **ä** far | **ō** open | **ch** child | e in taken |
| **e** let | **ô** order | **ng** long | i in pencil |
| **ē** equal | **oi** oil | **sh** she | o in lemon |
| **ėr** term | **ou** out | **th** thin | u in circus |
| **i** it | **u** cup | **TH** then | |
| | | **zh** measure | |

**fancy** (fan′sē), **1** picture to oneself; imagine: *Can you fancy yourself on the moon?* **2** power to imagine: *Elves are creatures of fancy.* **3** idea; notion; something imagined or thought of: *He had a sudden fancy to drive instead of going by plane.* **4** liking: *They took a great fancy to each other.* **5** not plain or simple; decorated: *fancy needlework, a fancy dinner for guests.* **6** requiring much skill: *fancy skating.* **7** of high quality or an unusual kind: *The shop offered a wide choice of fancy fruits for sale.*

**far** (fär), **1** a long way; a long way off: *She studied far into the night.* **2** not near; distant: *They live in a far country. The moon is far from the earth.* **3** more distant: *We live on the far side of the hill.* **4** much: *It is far better to go by train.*

**far·a·way** (fär′ə wā′), distant; far away: *He read about faraway places in his books.*

**fanciful** (definition 3)
I read a **fanciful** story
about a rose and
a butterfly.

## Practicing Using a Dictionary and Glossary

Read about old Boston and notice the underlined words. Where can you find more about those words?

When Molly Day came to <u>settle</u> in Boston, there was no such thing as a <u>hotel</u>.

1. Look up *settle* in your glossary.
2. What guide words are at the top of the page?
3. Read the entry for *settle*. How does the sentence help you understand the word better?
4. Could the word *seat* be on this page? Why?
5. Look up the word *hotel*. What guide words do you see on this page?
6. What does the entry for *hotel* say?
7. Could the word *hat* be on this page? Why?

## Tips for Reading on Your Own

- Use a dictionary or glossary to find the meaning of words you don't know.
- Check the guide words at the top of the page to see if your word fits alphabetically between them.
- Find your entry word on the page. Read the meaning.
- Use the sentence and the picture to help you understand the word.
- For other tips on figuring out words, see your Word Study Handbook.

*Although cities may be alike in some ways, they are quite different in other ways. As you read this article about two cities, think about what makes each city unique. See how each paragraph adds new ideas about the topic.*

# Two Great Cities

by Thelma Gruenbaum

A city is a large, busy place where many people live and work. Cities have offices, libraries, and schools. They have museums, restaurants, and stores. Although most cities have all these things, no two cities look the same. That is because each city mixes the old with the new in its own special way. Each city is unique.

Let's look at two great American cities, Boston and San Antonio. They are alike because both have many of the things that are usually found in a city. They are different because each has a different history. Part of what makes the histories of San Antonio and Boston different is where each city is found on the map.

## How Cities Change

Even though a city's place on the map doesn't change, the look of a city may change with time. As cities grow older they change just as people do. As more people live in a city, the city needs more space. Some buildings are torn down to make way for new ones. Many people say, "Keep the old ones too. Those buildings tell a story of our past."

Today, in Boston and in San Antonio, old buildings are being fixed up. People want to **restore** them. They want to look back at their history in the old buildings.

**restore,** fix to look the way it did when new.

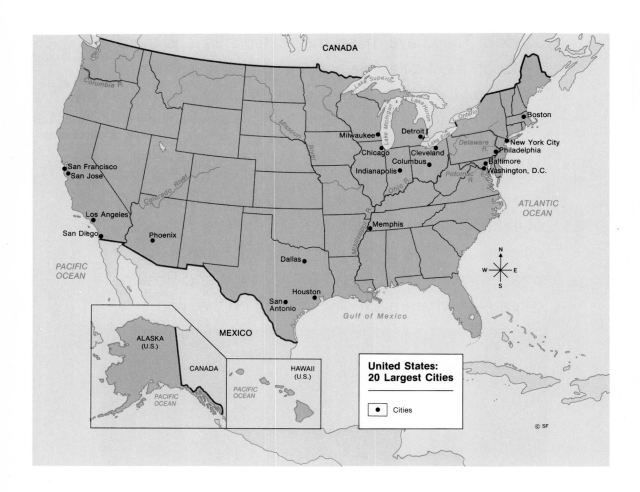

United States: 20 Largest Cities

• Cities

## Boston Then and Now

Boston was settled by people from England more than 350 years ago. The **settlers** in Boston lived on a **peninsula**. It was two miles long and one mile wide. In the middle were three mountains. Boston grew very fast. Soon there was no more space to build houses. Then someone had a great plan. Around the peninsula were **salt marshes**. The mountains could be cut down. Then dirt could be dumped into the water to make more land.

Much of Boston's **Back Bay** was made this way. Houses, big buildings, parks, and roads now stand where once there was water!

**settlers,** people who go to live in a new country.

**peninsula,** a piece of land with water almost all around it.

**salt marshes,** low lands filled with seawater; soft wet lands near the sea.

San Antonio's Spanish Governor's Palace restored to look as it did long ago.

## The Look of Old Boston

Long ago in Boston, houses were not built the way houses are built today. The oldest houses in Boston were put together with pegs of wood instead of nails. Fireplaces were used for heating and cooking. Because glass cost so much money, the windows were small. In a way, that was good. Small windows meant that less heat got out. But, with only candles for light, the houses were darker than houses of today.

Paul Revere's house is one of the oldest homes in Boston. When it was new, the house was two stories high. The Reveres had sixteen children, so they had to add a third floor. Years after the Revere family was gone, people remembered what Paul Revere had done for his country. They restored the house. Then they added furniture like that used by Paul Revere. Now it looks almost as it did when the Revere family lived there. Restoring old houses helps us learn how people lived in the early days of our country.

Paul Revere's house

Another building that shows what old Boston looked like is **Faneuil** (Fan'yəl) **Hall**, which was built for the city of Boston by Peter Faneuil. It was used as a market and as a town hall. In 1773, a group of men met at Faneuil Hall and decided to take a shipment of tea from a British ship and dump the tea into the harbor. That meeting at Faneuil Hall led to what we know as the Boston Tea Party. Because of that, Faneuil Hall has been called "The Cradle of Liberty."

There is a unique weather vane sitting on the bell tower of the hall. It is a copper grasshopper.

### The New Boston

Today, Faneuil Hall has been restored, and it is still used as a meeting place. It also is a part of what is called **Quincy Market**. The people of Boston are proud of Quincy Market with its many fine shops and places to eat. No matter what you have a taste for, you can probably find it there. Flowers can be seen everywhere in the market. At almost any time of day, people are there, walking or sitting on benches, and listening to music.

From Quincy Market, you can walk to the sea on a path of stones. There, at the waterside, you can see the docks, once old and dirty, now restored.

Watching people and seeing the sights are favorite pastimes at Quincy Market.

## Boston's Neighborhoods

People who come to a city from other countries help make life in the city more interesting. The city of Boston is lucky to have people from all over the world who have brought their music, food, and celebrations. Visitors to Boston enjoy two very special neighborhoods.

One special neighborhood is **Chinatown**. You know you're there when you pass through a fancy gate with figures of lions on either side. Even the phone booths here have brightly-colored curved roofs. The names of the streets are written in Chinese.

A good time to visit Chinatown is during the Chinese New Year celebration. There are parades with music, paper dragons, and firecrackers.

Another special neighborhood is the **North End** of Boston, which is an Italian neighborhood. Stores sell bread, pizza, and other Italian food. Like Chinatown, this neighborhood has special celebrations. One of the most famous is Columbus Day. Since Christopher Columbus was Italian, this holiday is very special in the North End.

## San Antonio Then and Now

The first Spanish settlers came to San Antonio more than 250 years ago. Like the settlers in Boston, the Spanish settlers in San Antonio built their homes near water. They laid out their town near the winding San Antonio River.

One day in 1921 it rained so much that the river spilled over its banks and flooded the city. People decided to save the river by building a dam. They dug new places for the river to go. Never again did the river flood the streets.

No longer are people afraid of the river. Now it draws many people to San Antonio. Along San Antonio's famous Riverwalk, or **Paseo del Rio,** are hotels, shops, and restaurants.

## The Look of Old San Antonio

Like Boston, San Antonio has many old and interesting buildings. Some people believe the most beautiful is the **Palace of the Spanish Governors.** But the most famous is the **Alamo.** For a time it was a school. Later it housed soldiers.

In March, 1836, there was a big battle at the Alamo. At that time, Texas was part of Mexico. The Texans wanted to end that. General Santa Ana, the ruler of Mexico, sent his soldiers to fight 188 Texans inside the Alamo. The battle went on for twelve days. Although the Texans lost that battle, Texas soon won its freedom from Mexico.

Because the Alamo is important in Texas history, the people of San Antonio have restored it to make it look as it did long ago. They have added a museum and a garden. You can learn a lot about Texas history there.

**adobe,** bricks that are made of clay baked in the sun.

Another interesting part of Texas history can be seen in **La Villita,** or "little village." Some of the houses here are made of **adobe.** They look like houses in Mexico. Some of the houses in La Villita look like houses in Germany and France. That's because German and French people came to live in them in the 1840s and 1850s.

Not long ago, when the houses at La Villita were restored, shops were added and artists came there to work. One of the newer buildings is a museum where objects about Texas history are on display.

The flags of Spain, France, Mexico, and the United States have flown over La Villita. They tell us something about San Antonio's history. Today half of the people in San Antonio speak Spanish. People from other lands have helped to make San Antonio's past rich and interesting.

A street in La Villita

## The New San Antonio

Like Boston, San Antonio looks to the future. The
**Tower of the Americas** is one of San Antonio's new
buildings. It was built for the **HemisFair,** or the Texas
World Fair, in 1968. The tower is so tall that from its
top you can see for 100 miles.

From the tower you can see the old farmer's market,
known as **El Mercado.** As you visit this market, you
can imagine the part Mexico played in San Antonio's
past. Things made in Texas and Mexico are sold here,
as well as food fresh from the farm. There are thirty
small, indoor shops at the market.

You can choose from many things at
El Mercado.

**fiesta,** a celebration with music and lots of food. There is often a parade during a fiesta.

All year long there are many **fiestas** with Mexican music and food.

The people of San Antonio love fiestas! Every spring there is the **Fiesta San Antonio** that lasts for ten days. Eight parades take place during this time. There is one parade to the Alamo. Another is a parade of decorated boats that float down the San Antonio River at night.

## Summing Up What You've Read

Cities are interesting places. The old and the new are side by side. People come from all over the world to visit or to live in cities like Boston and San Antonio. The people who come add their language, their music and art, and their celebrations to what the city already has. They make each city a unique place to live and learn.

# Comprehension Check

*Think and Discuss*

- **1.** What is the topic of this article?
  **2.** Name three unique places in Boston. Do the same for San Antonio.
- **3.** Reread the paragraph on page 111. Which of the following is the main idea of that paragraph?
  **a.** Boston and San Antonio are interesting cities.
  **b.** Cities are interesting places.
- **4.** What are two details you find on page 111?
  **5.** What do you think makes a city a special place to live?

- Comprehension Skill: Main idea and supporting details

# Communication Workshop

*Talk*

Pretend the oldest building in your town is the library. It is now too small to hold all the books. Should it be torn down? Discuss the issue with a group of classmates in a panel. Try to think of all the "pros" and "cons" you can. Then decide what *your* vote will be. What are your reasons?

Speaking/Listening: Panel discussion

*Write*

Write a brief radio ad that will make other people feel the way you do. Read it to the class.

Writing Fluency: Ad

# Picture As You Read

Your flying carpet lands you in Boston just outside Quincy Market. Since you have been flying all day, you are starving. You open the door to the market. Before you *see* anything, you *smell* melted cheese and fresh, green peppers. You know those things are on top of a freshly baked pizza. You know now what you are looking for because your sense of smell gives you a picture in your mind.

The same thing happens when you read. Words put pictures in your mind just as the smell of a good pizza can. Your mind uses the words on a page to make pictures of a character or setting. Those pictures help you understand and remember what you read.

Try making pictures in your mind as you read.

# Catching Quiet

by Marci Ridlon

It's hard to catch quiet
in the city.
You have to be quick.
It isn't around long.
You might find it
after the roar of a truck,
before a jet flies by.
You might find it
after the horns stop honking,
before the sirens start.
You might find it
after the ice-cream man's bell,
before your friends call you
to play.
But when you find it,
stick it in your heart fast.
Keep it there.
It's a bit of the sky.

*The City of Hub-Bub cannot be found on any map. One day something happens to bring a big change to Hub-Bub. Read to find out what that change is. As you read, ask yourself what you think makes a city a good place to live.*

# The **Loudest** Noise in the World

by Benjamin Elkin

Once upon a time the noisiest place in the world was a city called Hub-Bub. The people of Hub-Bub never talked, they yelled. They were very proud that their ducks were the quackiest, their doors the slammiest, and their police whistles the shrillest in the whole world.

Their favorite song was:

> Slam the door.
> Bang the floor.
> Days we roar,
> Nights we snore.
> Hub-Bub!

Of all the noisy people in Hub-Bub, the noisiest was a young prince named Hulla-Baloo. Even though he wasn't six years old yet, he could make more noise than the grown-ups. Hulla-Baloo loved to yell, bang pots and pans together, and blow a whistle—all at the same time.

His favorite game was to climb up a ladder, piling up trash cans and tin pails as high as he could, and then knock over the whole pile with a loud crash. He used to make the piles higher and higher, and they made louder and louder crashes.

But still he wasn't satisfied. Prince Hulla-Baloo wanted to hear the loudest noise in the world.

A few weeks before the prince's sixth birthday his father, the King of Hub-Bub, asked him what he wanted for a birthday present.

"I want to hear the loudest noise in the world," answered Hulla-Baloo.

"Fine," said the King. "I'll order the royal drummers to get out the special super-loud drums for the whole day."

"But I've heard them before," complained the prince. "That wouldn't be the loudest noise in the world."

"All right," promised the King. "I'll also order all policemen to blow their special super-loud whistles."

"I've already heard those too," said Hulla-Baloo. "They wouldn't be loud enough."

"Tell you what," said the King. "At the same time I'll close the schools and have the children stay home all day and slam the super-slammy doors. How's that?"

"That would help a lot," agreed the prince, "but it still wouldn't be the loudest noise in the world."

The King was a very kind father, but he began to lose his patience.

"What's on your mind?" he asked. "What great idea do you have?"

"Well," answered Prince Hulla-Baloo, "I'll tell you what I've been wanting for a long time. I want to hear every person in the world yell at the same minute. If millions and millions and millions of people all yelled together, I'm sure that would be the loudest noise in the world."

The more the King considered this idea, the better he liked it. "It might be fun," he thought. "And besides, I'll go down in history as the first king who ever got all the people in the whole world to do the same thing at the same time.

"Yes! I'll try it."

Then the King of Hub-Bub got busy. He sent out hundreds of messengers to visit every country, from the hottest jungles to the coldest ice lands. Every day thousands of messages were carried by telegraph and tom-tom, car and carrier pigeon, by airplane and dog sled.

And soon the answers began to pour in. Everybody was delighted with the idea, and all would be glad to help. The whole world seemed to be thrilled by the thought that every living person would be yelling at the very same time.

As the weeks passed and the birthday date grew nearer and nearer, the excitement grew greater and greater. In every country, people talked of nothing but Prince Hulla-Baloo's birthday. There wasn't a village in the world that didn't have a poster in its own language, giving the exact minute of local time at which to yell, "HAPPY BIRTHDAY!"

One afternoon, in a city far away, a woman was talking to her husband about Prince Hulla-Baloo's birthday.

"What bothers me," she said, "is how I'm going to hear everyone else yelling when I'm making so much noise myself. All I'll hear is my own voice."

"You're right," answered her husband. "When the time comes, let's open our mouths with the rest of the crowd, but we won't make a sound. Then, while all the others are shouting their heads off, we'll be quiet and really hear the noise."

That seemed to be a wonderful idea.

Without meaning any harm, the woman told her neighbors about her plan.

Without meaning any harm, her husband told his friends at the office where he worked. Still without meaning any harm, the friends told their friends, and those friends told other friends.

Before long, people all over the world, even in the City of Hub-Bub, were privately telling one another to open their mouths at the right time but not to yell, so they would be able to hear all the noise made by everyone else.

No one was trying to spoil the prince's birthday celebration. It was just that each person thought, "My voice won't be missed among so many millions. While all the others are yelling and screaming, it won't hurt if I stay quiet so I can really listen."

And so the important moment came closer and closer. In all corners of the earth crowds of people began gathering in their public meeting places. All over the world eyes stared at large clocks ticking away the seconds. It seemed that a shock of excitement, like electricity, swept around the entire globe. In Hub-Bub, of course, the excitement was especially great.

Thousands of people jammed the palace grounds, cheering and shouting, while high on the balcony the young prince waited happily for the loudest noise in the world.

Fifteen seconds to go . . . Ten seconds . . . Five seconds . . . NOW!

Two billion people strained their ears to catch the loudest noise in the world—and two billion people heard nothing but absolute silence.

Every person had kept quiet so he or she could hear the others yell, every person had expected the others to do the work while he or she sat back and enjoyed it.

What about the City of Hub-Bub, which had always been so proud of its noise? For the first time in a hundred years Hub-Bub too was silent and still. Instead of honoring their prince by the loudest noise in the world, they had belittled him by remaining absolutely quiet. The people bowed their heads in shame and started to creep away.

Suddenly they stopped. What was that sound they heard up in the balcony?

It couldn't be true! And yet there was the prince, clapping his hands in glee and laughing happily!

Sure enough, the prince was pointing to the garden with great delight.

For the first time in his life he was hearing the
singing of a little bird, the whispering of the wind in
the leaves, the ripple of the water in the brook. For
the first time in his life, he was hearing the sounds of
nature instead of the noise of Hub-Bub.

For the first time in his life the prince had been
given the gift of peace and quiet, and he loved it!

Now the City of Hub-Bub is noisy no more. Instead, visitors see this sign:

Welcome to Hub-Bub
The City of Quiet

The people of Hub-Bub speak gently. They are proud that their ducks are the quietest, their doors the lightest, and their police whistles the softest in the whole world.

## Meet the Author

When Benjamin Elkin was a small child, he was always making up stories and telling them to his friends. When he finished school he became a schoolteacher and then a principal; he kept on telling stories to children.

Benjamin Elkin left teaching to go off to be in the army. There were no children around to listen to his stories, so he began to write them down. His first story and the one that stayed his favorite was *The Loudest Noise in the World.*

A child once wrote to ask Elkin how many books he could write in one day. Elkin told him that it only seems easy to write a book. Really it is hard work that takes a long time.

Elkin gets his ideas from folk tales that have been told for years and years. He works for months, and sometimes years, to get old tales just right for young readers.

Some of Benjamin Elkin's other books are *Gillespie and the Guards, Six Foolish Fishermen, The Man Who Walked Around the World,* and *Lucky and the Giant.*

*Think and Discuss*

1. What big change happens in the City of Hub-Bub?
2. How does the King let the world know about the prince's birthday celebration?
3. What happens to change the King's plan?
• 4. Do you think the woman and her husband are right to say they won't yell when everyone else does? Why?
• 5. After reading this story, what do you think about telling other people something you don't want everyone to know?

● Comprehension Skill: Drawing conclusions

## Communication Workshop

*Talk*

Think up another funny city like Hub-Bub. For example, you might invent a city where there is the most color, or the most food, or where people walk backwards. Name your city. Then share your ideas with a partner. Spark your partner's imagination by asking questions about his or her city.

Speaking/Listening: Interviewing

*Write*

Reread the song of Hub-Bub on page 116. Write a song for your city like the song on page 116. Read your song aloud during a Class Song Fest.

Writing Fluency: Song

# LOOKING BACK

Prewriting

## Thinking and Writing About the Section

In this section you learned about old and new cities. Now imagine yourself in one. You can write a narrative paragraph to tell what you do there to share with a classmate. Copy the chart and fill it in with details.

*See your Thinker's Handbook for tips.*

| City | Old | New |
|------|-----|-----|
| New York | horses, gas lights, farms, corn | |
| Boston | | |
| San Antonio | | |
| Hub-Bub | | calm sounds: birds, wind, water |

**Writing**

Write a narrative paragraph that tells about one event that happens to you in the city. Use details from the chart and time order. For more help, see your Writer's Handbook.

**Revising**

Read your first draft to your partner. Have you used signal words to make the time order clear? Do you have details? Make changes, proofread, and then write your final copy.

**Presenting**

Find a classmate who wrote about the same city you did. Read your paragraphs to one another.

# 3

# Making Your Mark!

Making your mark isn't easy, but there are many ways of doing it. Some ways are big and important. Some ways are small, but may be just as important.

In this section you'll read about someone who made a big mark on American history, about someone who made a small but important mark in the lives of some creatures, and about someone who made his mark in a silly way by trying to be *too* important.

# Using an Encyclopedia

What was one of the first things you learned before you could read? If you think back, you will remember it was the **alphabet,** that special set of letters on which our language is built.

What makes this set of letters so special, and where did the idea of an alphabet begin? To find out, try looking in an encyclopedia.

An **encyclopedia** is a book or set of books with articles about many different things. A book in an encyclopedia set is called a **volume.** Each volume has a number and one or more letters on it. The volumes are in alphabetical order. Find the numbers and letters on the encyclopedia below.

An article in an encyclopedia is called an **entry.** At the beginning of each entry is a word in darker type called an **entry word.** The entry word tells what the article is about. An entry word may be only one word, or it may be more than one. All entry words begin with the letters shown on the outside of the volume and are in alphabetical order.

To look up an entry in the encyclopedia, find the volume in the encyclopedia that has the same letter as the first letter of your entry word. The entry word says what the article will be about. If you want to look up *alphabet,* look in the A volume, number 1.

If there are too many entries for one letter, the same letter may go on to another volume. All the entries in volumes 3 and 4 below begin with C. Use the second letter of an entry word to help you find the volume it is in. The entry *Cherokee* is in volume 3 because the name of this Indian tribe begins with ch.

Some volumes list two letters on the outside. Volume 14 below has entries that begin with both N and O. That is because there were not enough entry words starting with N or O to fill a whole volume.

**Guide words** can help you find an entry. A guide word is at the top of each page in an encyclopedia. Find the guide word on the encyclopedia page that follows.

The guide word on a left-hand page always names the first entry on that page. Here that guide word is **Alphabet.** The guide word on a right-hand page always names the last entry on that page. Here there is no other guide word because the entry for *Alphabet* is so long.

**┌─ Guide word**

**┌─ Entry word**

# ALPHABET

**ALPHABET,** *AL fuh beht,* is the series of letters used in writing a language. The name means exactly what the term ABC means as a name for the 26 letters of our alphabet. The word comes from *alpha* and *beta,* the first two letters of the Greek alphabet.

Most books, magazines, and newspapers are printed in the 26-letter alphabet called *Roman.* But the Romans did not invent it. They put finishing touches on a system that had been growing for thousands of years. See the articles on each letter of the English alphabet at the beginning of each letter in THE WORLD BOOK ENCYCLOPEDIA.

### The Earliest Writing

In early times, people could communicate with one another only by speaking or by making gestures. They had no way to keep records of important events, unless they memorized the story of a great battle or important happening. They had no way to send messages over long distances unless they passed them from one person to the next by word of mouth, or had one man memorize the message and then deliver it.

The first stage in writing came when men learned to draw pictures to express their ideas. In *ideography,* each picture conveyed an idea, and anyone could understand it, even if he did not know the language of the man who drew it. Then man learned *logography,* expressing ideas indirectly by using signs to stand for the words of the idea. Instead of drawing pictures of five sheep to show that he had five animals in his herd, a man could draw one sign for the numeral "five" and one for "sheep." Gradually man learned to use a *syllabic* system, in which a sign that stood for one word could be used not only for that word but also for any phonetic combination that sounded like that word. This is what we call *rebus writing* (see REBUS). If we used rebus writing

Bernadine Bailey

**The Egyptians** wrote with several hundred signs that stood for words or parts of words. The picture above shows an obelisk in Luxor, Egypt, carved with such word signs.

Deane Dickason, Ewing Galloway

**The Romans** wrote with an alphabet that stood for individual vowel and consonant sounds. Our alphabet is directly related to it. This inscription is cut into the stone of Rome's Pantheon.

366

## Practicing Using an Encyclopedia

1. Use the encyclopedia shown on page 134. In which volume would you find the entry, *Indian? Indian* starts with *I*. You would find the entry for *Indian* in the *I* volume, number 10.

2. Would *history* be between the guide words *hive* and *hobby?* No, the word *history* isn't between *hive* and *hobby* in alphabetical order. H–i–s–t–o–r–y comes before h–i–v–e.

3. In which volume on page 134 would you find the entry *Appalachian?*

4. Would the entry *language* be between these entry words: *landslide* and *lantern?* Explain your answer.

5. Could the entry *almond* be on the pages shown here? Why or why not?

## Tips for Reading on Your Own

- Remember that encyclopedia entries are in alphabetical order.
- Decide on the entry you want to look up.
- Remember all volumes are in alphabetical order.
- Decide which volume has the entry you are looking for.
- Use the guide words to find the entry.

*This is the true story of Sequoyah, who made his mark on history by solving a riddle. Read to find out what solving the riddle of the talking leaves meant.*

# Sequoyah and the Riddle of the Talking Leaves

by Alan Bickley

This is the true story of a man who gave a gift unlike any other to his people. It is the story of Sequoyah, the teacher, and the riddle of the talking leaves. It begins in the years before our country won its freedom from England.

The Cherokee people made their home in the east part of Tennessee. It was, to them, a place of matchless beauty. They hunted for game in the forests of the Appalachian Mountains. They farmed the valleys. To the west, beyond their lands, were the rivers that run toward the setting sun. The farms and villages of the new people who settled in this country were to the east of them.

In 1775, a child was born to a Cherokee woman named Wu-Teh. The child's father was Nathaniel Gist. He was a trader who had traveled those mountains for years. He named his son George because that was the name of his friend, George Washington. But George Gist lived among the Cherokee who called him Sequoyah.

By the time Sequoyah became a man, he could do many things. He could make tools of iron. He was a builder, a hunter, and a farmer. But today we remember and respect him for something else, something unique.

The Cherokee were a people of great talent. They understood numbers and how the stars moved. They were fine singers, and they kept the history of their nation in songs. They knew what to do for people who were sick. What they did not have was a way of writing their language.

In 1812 the people of the United States went to war against England. The Cherokee sided with the Americans. Like many other men of the Cherokee Nation, Sequoyah left his wife and children and went away to fight. The life of a soldier was dangerous and lonely. For two years Sequoyah heard nothing of his family. That was not true of the American soldiers. They knew what was happening in their families. Papers would come with black marks on them. When the soldiers looked at the marks, they might laugh or they might become very thoughtful. Sometimes they would cry.

Some soldiers could send their thoughts home. They made ink from a formula of roots and berries cooked with iron. Then, with a duck's feather, they would make marks on paper. A special carrier would take the papers to the families of the soldiers. This was how many soldiers talked to their loved ones even though they were far apart.

Of course, some soldiers could not make the marks. They would tell a friend what they wished to say, and the friend would use the feather. One soldier would talk, and one would mark. Talking and marking, thought Sequoyah. How remarkable! The marks stood for words, and the words were made of sounds. The papers were like dry leaves that carried talk. Sequoyah was beginning to understand their secret.

Sequoyah came home a changed man. He worked on his farm. He made tools for those who wished to buy them, but he cared less and less for that kind of work. More and more, he left that work to his sons. The riddle of the talking leaves never left his mind. He would listen carefully to the talk all around him. He would think up a mark to stand for each sound. Then he would draw the marks on pieces of tree bark. Once he made three marks that he showed to his child, Ahyoka (Ah–yo–ka). Sequoyah said, "That is your name."

For two years, Sequoyah worked to find a sign for every sound in the Cherokee language. He filled hundreds of pieces of bark with his marks. As it happens when someone gives so much of his time to one thing, he became careless about the rest of his life. The house was falling apart. Sequoyah seemed to pay no attention. His wife would often lose her temper. One day holes began to appear in the roof.

"When will you cover those holes?" his wife would ask.

"Later," Sequoyah would say. "Right now I must find a sign for *roof* and a sign for *holes.*"

That was it for Sequoyah's wife. She gathered the bunches of bark into her hands and threw them into the fire. Within seconds they were ashes.

"Now get out, worthless one!" his wife raged. "You are of no more use here."

Sequoyah said nothing. He got two blankets and, taking Ahyoka with him, left his house for good.

Sequoyah and Ahyoka spent the next year living in a small house in the woods. He hunted game. Ahyoka did the cooking and took care of the house. At night, by firelight, Sequoyah recalled the signs that had vanished in the flames. When the year was up, he had covered a deer skin with the signs. Now he could roll up the skin and carry it wherever he went. The signs he wrote on the bark would be safe. He would never lose them again.

### Cherokee Alphabet.

| | | | | | |
|---|---|---|---|---|---|
| D a | R e | T i | ꝺ o | ꮟ u | i v |
| S ga Ꭴ ka | Ɏ ge | ꭹ gi | A go | J gu | E gv |
| Ꮂ ha | P he | Ꭷ hi | Ꮅ ho | Ꮿ hu | Ꮀ hv |
| W la | Ꮯ le | P li | G lo | M lu | � lv |
| Ꮆ ma | Ꮹ me | Ꮒ mi | ꮝ mo | Ꮿ mu | |
| O na Ꮑ hna G nah | Ꭺ ne | h ni | Z no | Ꮖ nu | C nv |
| Ꮖ qua | Ꮃ que | Ꮅ qui | Ꮴ quo | Ꮻ quu | Ɛ quv |
| U sa Ꭴ s | Ꮞ se | Ꮈ si | Ꮦ so | Ꭶ su | R sv |
| Ꮮ da Ꮃ ta | Ꮪ de Ꮫ te | Ꮫ di Ꮧ ti | V do | Ꮪ du | Ᏻ dv |
| Ꮥ dla Ꮮ tla | L tle | C tli | Ꮹ tlo | Ꮩ tlu | P tlv |
| Ꮐ tsa | Ꮡ tse | Ir tsi | K tso | J tsu | Ꮳ tsv |
| G wa | Ꮼ we | Ꮎ wi | Ꮼ wo | Ꮄ wu | 6 wv |
| Ꮽ ya | Ꮟ ye | ꮞ yi | Ꮂ yo | Ꮖ yu | B yv |

Now it happened that the American settlers moved west and found gold where the Indian people were living. The Cherokee were forced to leave their homeland and move west. Those Cherokee who survived the trip became the west branch of the Cherokee Nation in Arkansas and in what is now called Oklahoma. At first, Sequoyah stayed in Tennessee, hiding in the mountains. As things changed, he grew restless in his old home. At last he packed his belongings. He and Ahyoka set out for the west branch of the Cherokee Nation.

At the end of their long trip, someone new came into their lives. Sequoyah married a Cherokee woman named Sally. With her young son and Ahyoka, they settled on a farm near what is now the town of Sallisaw, Oklahoma. Sequoyah kept on working on his signs. Sally gave him the courage to carry on his search for new words.

At first the family played a game with the signs. One of them would leave the room, and the others would write messages using Sequoyah's signs. Then that person would return and tell the others what was written on the piece of bark. When Sally went away to visit her parents in Arkansas, she wrote Sequoyah letters. He would read the letters to the children.

It was becoming clear that the family game was something that ought to be shared with all of the Cherokee Nation. Sequoyah decided that he must return east to offer the secret of the talking leaves to his people.

The chief of the Cherokees was John Ross. He had been to school at Dartmouth College, and he could understand many languages. But he could not write his own Cherokee language.

No one could, except Sequoyah, Sally, her son, and Ahyoka. When Ahyoka and her father came to John Ross's home in the Eastern Nation, Ross listened. He was a reasonable man. It was clear that Sequoyah's ideas were the kind that deserved attention. Ross made a plan for a test.

The test was to be like the family game, only it was to be played before the most important men of the Nation. The chiefs sent Sequoyah out of the house where they were meeting. Ahyoka stayed behind. One by one, they asked her to write of things that only they could know. In a clear, sure hand, Ahyoka wrote on the papers before her.

Thirty minutes later, Ross asked Sequoyah back to read what they had told Ahyoka to write.

Sequoyah's eyes quickly read the paper. His mouth shaped the words written there. When he finished, he looked up at the joyous Ahyoka. The chiefs of his Nation were amazed. They rushed toward him to shake his hand. He had passed the test. The Cherokees had a written language.

Sequoyah invented a written language based on the spoken language of his people. A written language meant that the Cherokee people could have their own schools and newspapers. They could now send letters to each other. Even in hard times, they would have a way to stay together and know what was happening to each other. A written language would help to unite them.

For Sequoyah, the search for understanding and learning was not at an end. Years later he traveled into Mexico searching to find the roots of the Cherokee language. He died there. The site of his grave is not known.

When Oklahoma became a state, its people showed their respect for Sequoyah by placing a statue of him in a building in Washington. The people of Oklahoma thought of him as their greatest son. A county is named for him. On the west coast of the United States, the giant sequoia trees carry his name. They stand tall above the land around them, as tall as the teacher, Sequoyah, stands in history.

## Meet the Author

The Cherokees moved to Oklahoma from their old homes in east Tennessee with a promise of new land. Part of that land lay between Kansas on the north and what was called Indian Territory on the south and east. This land was called the Cherokee Strip. In 1893 the Cherokee Strip was opened to anyone who was willing to settle there. The grandmother of the author of this selection was one of the first settlers. With her husband, she helped to build the town where Alan Bickley was born.

Alan Bickley remembered the story of Sequoyah from his school days. He was eager to write about the great Cherokee teacher.

Since he was in junior high school, Alan Bickley has worked in television and in radio. He has been a news writer and a radio newscaster in Dallas, in Boston, with the U.S. Army in Japan, and now in Chicago.

Many Indian tribes moved to Oklahoma after losing their lands in other parts of the country. Alan Bickley says, "It is exciting to study history. I believe there is much that all of us can learn from the Indians' history. It tells how people can live together and govern themselves."

# Comprehension Check

*Think and Discuss*

1. What does it mean to the Cherokee people that Sequoyah solves the riddle of the talking leaves?
2. Why is Sequoyah unable to get news of his family during the War of 1812?
3. How does Sequoyah prove to the chiefs of his Nation that the marks on the bark have meaning?
 • 4. Look back at the encyclopedia volumes on page 134. Which volume would you use to find out more about: (a) Sequoyah; (b) the Cherokee Strip; (c) Oklahoma?

*See your Thinker's Handbook for tips.*

• Study Skill: Encyclopedia

# Communication Workshop

*Talk*

Imagine your life with no writing in it. Discuss with a partner how your lives would be different if you could not read or write at all. What other ways could you communicate?

Speaking/Listening: Cooperative learning

*Write*

Divide a chart into three parts and label them *Home*, *School*, and *Other*. Write the ways you use writing in your life. Then compare your chart with your partner's.

Writing Fluency: Chart

*Fiona loves animals so much that she leaves a dog dish full of water out just in case a dog might come by. One day a dog does come by. Read to find out how this stray dog leads Fiona to make her mark.*

# Fiona's Flea

by Beverly Keller

Fiona Foster lay on the floor looking at the funnies and worrying her mother and father. "You can't walk around being sad all day and think that we'll take you to the circus tonight," her mother warned. "And how would you feel if you missed the circus?"

Fiona did not look up, but she whispered, "Glad."

"What did she say?" her father asked.

"She said she'd feel bad," Fiona's mother told him.

"I thought she said *mad*."

Mrs. Foster frowned. "Maybe she said *sad*."

Fiona looked up from a book. "I said glad."

"No, no," her father said. "We're talking about how you'd feel if you *missed* the circus."

"Glad," Fiona said once more.

"Fiona," Mrs. Foster said, "every child loves a circus."

"I don't," Fiona said. She saw that they were quite surprised. "Maybe I'd better go to the park now, so you can talk about me while I'm not around."

Barbara and Larry and Howard were at the park. Howard's dog Spike was on a leash. Barbara's brother Oliver was in a stroller, trying to chew Spike's leash.

"What are you going to wear to the circus?" Barbara asked Fiona.

"I'm not going," Fiona said.

Larry looked at her with respect. "You must have done something really terrible to be kept home from the circus!"

"I don't want to go," Fiona said.

Larry was amazed. "You mean you don't want to see all the lions and tigers?"

Fiona watched a bug wander across the path. "Lions and tigers do not belong in cages."

Barbara looked worried. "But what about the elephants? You'll miss all the elephants."

"With chains on their legs?" Fiona watched Spike roll in the grass. "Elephants put up with too much."

"All right. Forget elephants," Barbara said. "How about the clowns? You can't have anything against clowns."

Fiona shivered. "They have scary faces and their shoes make me nervous."

"You just want to ruin everything for everybody else, Fiona Foster!"

Barbara jumped up and wheeled Oliver away. Larry and Howard left with Spike. Fiona went home.

She filled her dog dish with water and put it on the porch, in case some dog dropped by for a drink. Then she sat on the porch steps eating old grapes.

A thin, sad, stray dog wandered near. "Have a drink," Fiona said.

He scrunched down on the sidewalk and waited for her to throw something at him. A stray dog, and not very good-looking, he was used to being yelled at and chased. He knew it was no use to run. Things people threw went faster than he could.

"Have a grape," Fiona said.

Dogs do not eat grapes. But this dog had not eaten for a long time. A grape was something. He crawled a little closer. He looked nervous as he chewed on a grape. Then he ate the bunch. After he lapped up the water, he stepped in the dog dish. Then he sat on the step and leaned against Fiona.

Her mother and father came out. "Get that flea-bitten dog off our porch," her father ordered.

The dog leaped off the step and walked around the corner.

"You didn't have to be mean to him!" Fiona cried.

"He was covered with fleas," her mother said.

Fiona ran after the stray. When she found him, he was shivering. After she had petted him for a little while, he followed her to the park and sat watching her think. When Fiona saw her friends coming, she put her arm around him so he wouldn't run again.

"That's the worst-looking, old, flea-bitten dog I ever saw," Larry said.

"He'd better not get fleas all over Spike," Howard warned.

Barbara held Oliver back. "I don't want any fleas on my brother. He'd eat them."

Fiona hugged the stray.

"You're going to get fleas," Larry told her.

"Look! Look! Look!" Barbara pointed. "She's got one!"

A tiny flea had moved onto Fiona's arm.

"Squash it before it bites," Barbara said.

Fiona stared at the flea, which was barely big enough to see. "Oliver bites, and nobody squashes him."

"He's too big," Barbara said.

Howard frowned at the flea. "Shake it off on the grass."

Fiona waited and watched. "Do fleas live on grass?"

"They die on grass," Larry said. "They only live on animals—or people."

Fiona looked down at the flea. She pictured that poor thing lost in a grass jungle, dying alone, with nobody to hold its flea hand—or foot.

"Why don't you put it back on the dog?" Barbara said.

Fiona looked carefully at the dog. "Don't fleas bite dogs?"

"Sure. And dogs scratch fleas," Larry said.

The flea was hardly more than a dot, and the dog's claws were long and large. "That could be hard on the flea."

Fiona felt a tiny sharp itch on her arm. "I think it bit me."

Barbara grabbed Oliver's stroller. "I don't want my brother near a person who has fleas!"

"Take Spike with you, Barbara," Howard said. "I'm not having my dog around any flea-bitten person."

Fiona closed her eyes and wished she were anybody else—even Oliver—even a *clown.*

"Listen, Fiona," Howard said, "you can't keep that flea on you. How will you feel when word gets around? How will you feel when it's written on all the sidewalks—*Fiona Foster wears fleas?*"

Fiona clapped her flea-free hand over her ear.

"There's no place you can go with a flea all over you—except maybe a flea circus," he went on.

Fiona took her hand off her ear. "Flea circus?"

"They used to have them in the old days," Larry said. "There were fleas in little tents doing tricks."

Fiona opened her eyes. "You mean people tamed these tiny things with whips?"

"Come *on.*" Howard snorted. "A whip would wipe out the whole circus."

"This was more of a show than a circus," Larry said. "A flea show was probably the only place in the world where a flea wouldn't be sprayed, or squashed, or scratched."

Fiona felt another small nip on her arm.

"I don't suppose they still have flea shows anymore."

"There's a flea market down by the bus station," Howard reminded her.

"Sometimes you are really silly," Larry said. "They sell old furniture and junk at flea markets. Nobody sells *fleas.*"

Fiona scratched, carefully. "It wouldn't hurt just to walk down there."

Larry went home. The stray dog followed Howard and Fiona to the flea market.

"You talk while I stay back," Fiona told Howard. "I don't know how people would feel having a real flea around."

Howard found a man near a stand full of old dishes and broken clocks. "Um . . . I'm wondering about fleas."

The man looked down at him. "You want to buy a *flea?*"

"I just wanted to know about a flea circus."

The man smiled. "Son, there has not been a flea circus in this town in years."

Howard and Fiona and the dog were scuffing across the road when they heard behind them, "FLEA CIRCUS!" The man caught up with them. "What an idea! I've been running that flea market for years and I never thought of it. Just think—the first flea market in the world to have a great and glorious, old-time, real American *flea circus!* But what am I talking about? You can't find a flea with manners these days." He trudged back toward his flea market.

"I didn't mean to ruin his day." Howard looked at the flea bites on Fiona's arm. "There's one last chance. Maybe an animal trainer would know how fleas used to be tamed."

"You mean a trainer from the big circus?"

"Look, Fiona. There could be some nice way to teach a flea not to bite."

A woman who was standing nearby looked up. She seemed to know the flea market very well. "You're not going to find anybody who trains fleas anymore. The last person I knew who trained fleas was my daddy, when we had our flea show."

"Was it like a flea circus?" Fiona asked.

"Never! We didn't keep our fleas in a cage, like animals."

"I suppose they'd just walk out between the bars," Howard said.

The woman nodded. "Besides, if you don't treat a flea just right, he'll die on you."

"*On* you?" Fiona looked down at her arm.

"Oh, a flea doesn't ask for much, just a cozy space, a little nip from a friendly person. But why am I going on like this? Nobody cares about fleas anymore."

"The man who runs the flea market does," Fiona said. "He wants a flea circus."

The woman grabbed Fiona's arm. "He does?"

"Look out!" Fiona cried. "My flea!"

The woman let go and looked carefully at the flea. "He's all right. Poor dear! How could anyone hurt a flea? But tell me about this man."

Fiona did. "You don't suppose he could use a flea *show*?" the woman asked.

"Of course he could," Howard said.

"Just let me fix myself up." The woman ran a piece of comb through her hair. "I know I could put together a great show. After all, I ought to know. I grew up with fleas!"

They found the man near a table of old books. "We brought you a famous flea trainer!" Howard said.

The woman brushed dust off her dress. "My name is Mardella Wax. I may not look like much, but, believe me, I know fleas."

"I could tell that the minute I set eyes on you."
Taking them to an old stand, the man bought them
each a big, warm pretzel.

He and Mardella talked fleas and business, and
finally shook hands. He gave Howard and Fiona a
bag of popcorn, fed the stray another pretzel, and
said, "See you Saturday," to Mardella Wax.

"Just one more thing," Mardella said. "After this,
my dog gets nothing but the best."

The man looked surprised. "Your dog?"

"From now on he is. You can see he needs a
person." She leaned over the stray and parted
his fur.

"Look at those fleas. All that talent, just trying to
get by in the dust and dirt. Once I've coaxed them
off him, I'll give him a bath and some good food.
He'll sit outside my ticket stand and call people over.
Every good show needs a barker."

"How will you keep the fleas off him?" Fiona asked.

Mardella Wax patted the stray very carefully. "In a
week, these fleas wouldn't be caught dead on a dog.
You'll see. You'll be my special guests when it's
showtime."

Fiona held out her arm. "What about this one?"

Mardella Wax looked closely at Fiona's flea. "This
one? Anybody with half an eye could see that *this*
one was born to be a star. Come along, you little
nipper."

Howard watched her leave, the flea on her hand, the dog following her. "Do you think we did the right thing?" he asked Fiona.

"I hope so," Fiona said, "since we couldn't think of anything else."

When she got home, her mother and father were cross.

"You say you won't go to a circus, you chase after stray dogs, then you come home scratching like a monkey and carrying a bag of popcorn," her father stormed.

"Half a bag," she explained.

"Get right in the tub," her mother ordered.

As Fiona lay back scratching in a sea of bubbles, her mother came into the bathroom.

"My goodness! Did you use all the bubble bath?"

"I deserve it." Fiona stretched her toes. "I saved a life, and I got dozens more into show business."

**Think and Discuss**

1. How does the stray dog lead Fiona to make her mark?
2. What kind of person do you think Fiona is? Find sentences in the story to back up your answer.
3. How do Howard, the man at the flea market, and Mardella Wax all help Fiona make her mark?
4. If you were Fiona, what might you say to your parents to help them understand you?
- 5. Tell what each underlined word stands for below.
   a. A tiny flea settled on Fiona's wrist. "Squash <u>it</u> before <u>it</u> bites," Barbara said.
   b. Fiona said, "Oliver bites, and nobody squashes <u>him</u>."

- Comprehension Skill; Referents

# Communication Workshop

**Talk**

Fiona thinks circuses are bad places for animals. Do you agree? Share your reasons with a partner.

Speaking/Listening: Discussion

**Write**

Make a list of three reasons why you think Fiona is right or wrong. Use your list to enter a debate with a small group of your classmates.

Writing Fluency: List

# Taking a Test

Ted decided to make his mark by doing well on his reading test. He thought the way to do that was to do all the test items very fast. So Ted read the directions.

"Fill in the circle next to the word that has the *same* or *almost the same* meaning as the word at the top of each item."

Here is how Ted did the first two items.

**1. quiet**
- ○ rapid
- ● noisy
- ○ peaceful

**2. amaze**
- ○ corn
- ◉ plant
- ○ surprise

What did Ted do wrong? In the first item, Ted did not read the directions carefully. In the second item, Ted did not work carefully. You don't have to make the mistakes Ted made. Just follow these tips:

- Read directions carefully.
- Read all the choices before you write.
- Mark your answers clearly.
- If the test is timed, do the items you know and then go back to the other items if there is time.

# Philbert Phlurk

by Jack Prelutsky

The major quirk of Philbert Phlurk
was tinkering all day,
inventing things that didn't work,
a scale that wouldn't weigh,
a pointless pen that couldn't write,
a score of silent whistles,
a bulbless lamp that wouldn't light,
a toothbrush with no bristles.

He built a chair without a seat,
a door that wouldn't shut,
a cooking stove that didn't heat,
a knife that couldn't cut.
He proudly crafted in his shop
a wheel that wouldn't spin,
a sweepless broom, a mopless mop,
a stringless violin.

He made a million useless things
like clocks with missing hands,
like toothless combs and springless springs
and stretchless rubber bands.
When Phlurk was through with something new,
he'd grin and say with glee,
"I know this does not work for you,
but ah! it works for me."

*Yertle the Turtle was king of all he could see. His problem was that he didn't think he saw enough. Read to find out how Yertle makes his mark.*

# Yertle the Turtle

by Dr. Seuss

CLASSIC

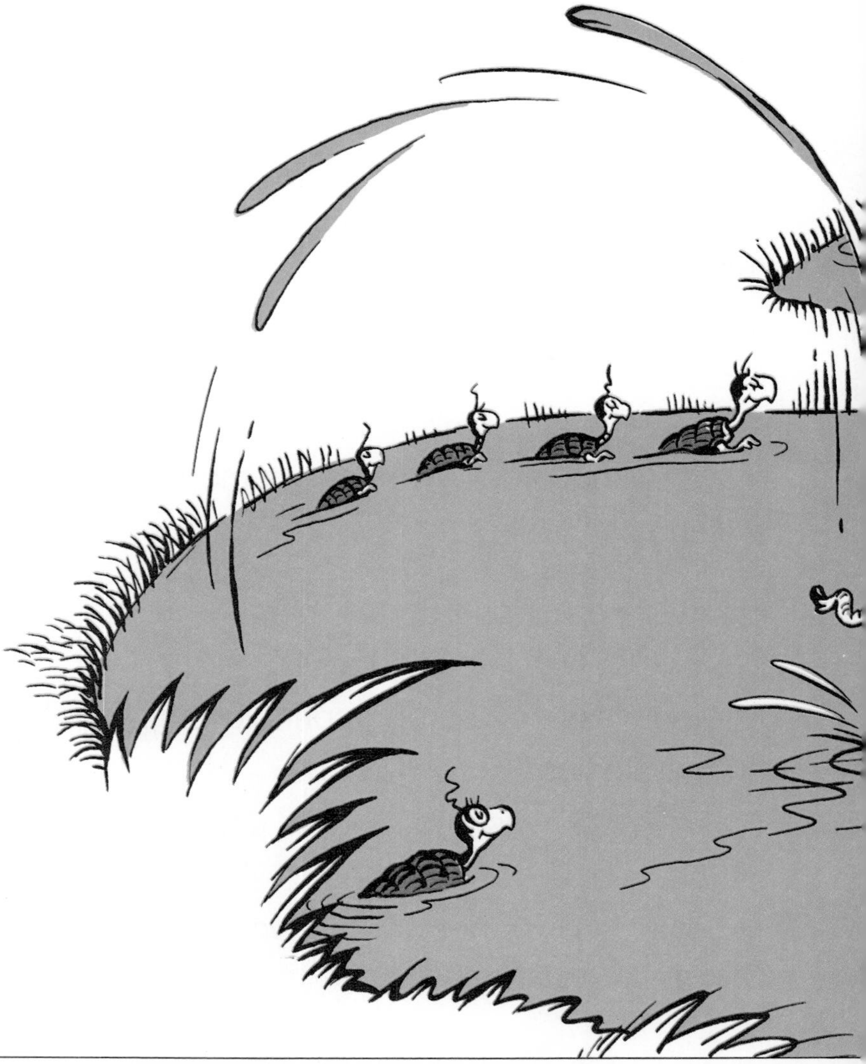

On the far-away Island of Sala-ma-Sond,
Yertle the Turtle was king of the pond.
A nice little pond. It was clean. It was neat.
The water was warm. There was plenty to eat.
The turtles had everything turtles might need.
And they were all happy. Quite happy indeed.

They *were* . . . until Yertle, the king of them all,
Decided the kingdom he ruled was too small.
"I'm ruler," said Yertle, "of all that I see.
But I don't see *enough*. That's the trouble with me.
With this stone for a throne, I look down on my pond
But I cannot look down on the places beyond.
This throne that I sit on is too, too low down.
It ought to be *higher!*" he said with a frown.
"If I could sit high, how much greater I'd be!
What a king! I'd be ruler of all I could see!"

So Yertle, the Turtle King, lifted his hand.
And Yertle, the Turtle King, gave a command.
He ordered nine turtles to swim to his stone
And, using these turtles, he built a *new* throne.
He made each turtle stand on another one's back
And he piled them all up in a nine-turtle stack.
And then Yertle climbed up. He sat down on the pile.
What a wonderful view! He could see 'most a mile!

"All mine!" Yertle cried. "Oh, the things I now rule!
I'm king of a cow! And I'm king of a mule!
I'm king of a house! And, what's more, beyond that,
I'm king of a blueberry bush and a cat!
I'm Yertle the Turtle! Oh, marvelous me!
For I am the ruler of all that I see!"

And all through that morning, he sat there up high
Saying over and over, "A great king am I!"
Until 'long about noon. Then he heard a faint sigh.
"What's *that?*" snapped the king
And he looked down the stack.
And he saw, at the bottom, a turtle named Mack.
Just a part of his throne. And this plain little turtle
Looked up and he said, "Beg your pardon, King Yertle.
I've pains in my back and my shoulders and knees.
How long must we stand here, Your Majesty, please?"

"SILENCE!" The King of the Turtles barked back.
"I'm king, and you're only a turtle named Mack.
 You stay in your place while I sit here and rule.
 I'm king of a cow! And I'm king of a mule!
 I'm king of a house! And a bush! And a cat!
 But that isn't all. I'll do better than *that!*
 My throne shall be *higher!*"  his royal voice thundered.
"So pile up more turtles! I want 'bout two hundred!"

"Turtles! More turtles!" he bellowed and brayed.
 And the turtles 'way down in the pond were afraid.
 They trembled. They shook. But they came. They obeyed.
 From all over the pond, they came swimming by dozens.
 Whole families of turtles, with uncles and cousins.
 And all of them stepped on the head of poor Mack.
 One after another, they climbed up the stack.

THEN Yertle the Turtle was perched up so high,
He could see forty miles from his throne in the sky!
"Hooray!" shouted Yertle. "I'm king of the trees!
I'm king of the birds! And I'm king of the bees!
I'm king of the butterflies! King of the air!
Ah, me! What a throne! What a wonderful chair!
I'm Yertle the Turtle! Oh, marvelous me!
For I am the ruler of all that I see!"

Then again, from below, in the great heavy stack,
Came a groan from that plain little turtle named Mack.
"Your Majesty, please . . . I don't like to complain,
But down here below, we are feeling great pain.
I know, up on top you are seeing great sights,
But down at the bottom we, too, should have rights.
We turtles can't stand it. Our shells will all crack!
Besides, we need food. We are starving!" groaned Mack.

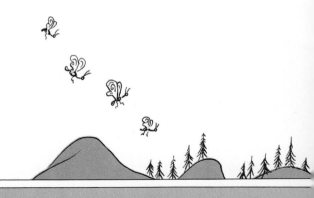

"You hush up your mouth!" howled the mighty King
    Yertle.
"You've no right to talk to the world's highest turtle.
  I rule from the clouds! Over land! Over sea!
  There's nothing, no NOTHING, that's higher than me!"

  But, while he was shouting, he saw with surprise
  That the moon of the evening was starting to rise
  Up over his head in the darkening skies.
"What's THAT?" snorted Yertle. "Say, what IS that thing
  That dares to be higher than Yertle the King?
  I shall not allow it! I'll go higher still!
  I'll build my throne higher! I can and I will!
  I'll call some more turtles. I'll stack 'em to heaven!
  I need 'bout five thousand, six hundred and seven!"

BURP!

But, as Yertle the Turtle King, lifted his hand
And started to order and give the command,
That plain little turtle below in the stack,
That plain little turtle whose name was just Mack,
Decided he'd taken enough. And he had.
And that plain little lad got a little bit mad.
And that plain little Mack did a plain little thing.
*He burped!*
And his burp shook the throne of the king!

And Yertle the Turtle, the king of the trees,
The king of the air, and the birds and the bees,
The king of a house and a cow and a mule. . . .
Well, *that* was the end of the Turtle King's rule!
For Yertle, the King of all Sala-ma-Sond,
Fell off his high throne and fell *Plunk!* In the pond!

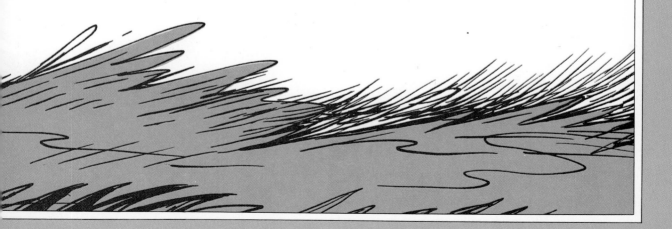

And today the great Yertle, that Marvelous he,
Is King of the Mud. That is all he can see.
And the turtles, of course . . . all the turtles are free
As turtles and, maybe, all creatures should be.

## Meet the Author and Illustrator

As a young boy, Theodor Seuss Geisel was always drawing pictures of funny animals. He kept drawing as he grew older, even after people who knew something about art told him that he would never make his mark as an artist. Today Theodor Seuss Geisel is known and loved as Dr. Seuss, the writer of many children's books.

Drawing is fun for Dr. Seuss, but writing has always been very hard work. He has written a story as many as twenty times before feeling happy with it. "I know my stuff looks like it was done in 23 seconds," he says, "but every word is a struggle."

Writing may be a struggle, but Dr. Seuss has made his mark on young readers. His books have made reading a wonderful, marvelous thing to do.

Besides using the name Dr. Seuss, Theodor Geisel has written books as Theo Le Sieg. Some of his best known books are *And to Think That I Saw It on Mulberry Street, The 500 Hats of Bartholomew Cubbins, Horton Hatches the Egg,* and *Green Eggs and Ham.*

## Thinking and Writing About the Section

| Prewriting |
| --- |

*See your Thinker's Handbook for tips.*

In this section, you read about characters who made their marks. Use their experiences to help you think of a time when *you* made your mark. You can write about it in a personal experience narrative to share with a friend. Copy the chart and fill it in.

| Person | How He/She Made a Mark | Result |
| --- | --- | --- |
| Sequoyah | | Cherokees can read. |
| Fiona | | |
| Yertle | | |
| You! | | |

| Writing |
| --- |

Now write about a time you made your mark. Tell the events in order and include your thoughts and feelings. Check your Writer's Handbook for more help in narrative writing.

| Revising |
| --- |

Read your first draft to a friend. Is it clear what mark you made and how you felt about it? Make changes and proofread. Then write a final copy.

| Presenting |
| --- |

Share your personal experience narrative with a friend who was there or remembers the event.

# Books to Read

**Squash Pie** by Wilson Gage

Someone is stealing the farmer's squash. The farmer tries to catch the thief by planting different vegetables—even dogwood trees. What can he be thinking?

**Fiona's Bee** by Beverly Keller

Fiona is too shy to meet new people until a bee finds her. Then Fiona's buzzing "pet" helps her to make a lot of friends.

**Sandra Day O'Connor** by Carol Greene

Sandra Day O'Connor made her mark on American history by being the first woman to sit on the Supreme Court. In this biography, you can read about her life and how she worked to make her plans and her dreams come true.

**The Conversation Club** by Diane Stanley

Peter Fieldmouse's new neighbors invite him to join their Conversation Club. What a surprise it is to find that their idea of conversation is to have everyone talk at once. While teaching his neighbors an important lesson about listening, Peter learns something about himself.

# 4

# Getting There

What do your legs, a pogo stick, a wheelchair, a wild horse, and a rocket have in common? They are all ways to get from one place to another.

Some people say that "getting there" is half the fun of a journey. As you read this section, you'll learn about a hero of the Old West, a runner, a fighter for the disabled, and a space crew. They'll give you a new view of "getting there."

# Similes and Metaphors

Russ remembers the first time he tried to ice skate. His feet were like runaway rockets. His arms were windmills.

When you picture Russ skating, do you think he has rockets on his feet? Are his arms really windmills? No. Writers often compare two very different things so readers see things in a new way. You understand how hard it was for Russ to skate when you imagine his feet seeming to run away like rockets and his arms waving like windmills.

In the paragraph above, the writer used the word *like* to compare Russ's feet to rockets. Comparisons that use the word *like* or the word *as* are **similes.**

When the writer says that Russ's arms were windmills, you know the writer is comparing Russ's arms to windmills, but there is no signal word, such as *like* or *as.* That comparison is a **metaphor.** Writers use similes and metaphors so you picture what they are saying more clearly in your mind.

Read about Jessie's new way to travel. Watch for examples of similes and metaphors.

A pogo stick! What would Uncle Fred think of next? Jessie decided to try her uncle's gift right away. On Jessie's first try, she toppled over like a dead tree. Then she did a few careful hops. Soon, Jessie was a bouncing kangaroo.

1. Read the fourth sentence. What two things is the writer comparing?

Did you say the writer compared Jessie to a dead tree when she fell over? It is easy to understand how Jessie fell when you compare her fall to the way a dead tree would fall over.

2. What kind of comparison is that? How do you know?

Did you say that it is a simile because it uses the word *like?* Remember that the words *like* and *as* tell you when a comparison is a simile.

3. Does the writer really think that Jessie is a kangaroo?

4. What kind of a comparison is the writer using when he says, "Jessie was a bouncing kangaroo"?

## Practicing Finding Similes and Metaphors

Read the paragraphs below about flying in a hot air balloon. Watch for similes and metaphors.

Toby looked over the edge of the balloon's basket. The balloon was like a cloud carrying her through the sky. She saw people as tiny as ants. Rivers were long silver strings. The grass was a green blanket covering the hills.

Sam untied two sand bags and the balloon shot up like a rocket. Later, the balloon was a feather, gently falling to earth.

1. What two things are compared in the second sentence? How are they alike?
2. Which metaphor in the second paragraph tells about the trip back down to earth? What two things are compared?
3. How many similes are in the two paragraphs above? How many metaphors?

## Tips for Reading on Your Own

- Think about how a writer uses comparisons to help you see things in a new way.
- When you find a simile or a metaphor, think about what two things are being compared.
- Ask yourself how the things are alike or different.

*Amazing tales are told of Pecos Bill, a hero of the
Old West. People thought Bill could ride anything,
but they never thought he'd have to ride a tornado.
Read to find out what Bill does when a tornado
takes off with his ranch. Notice how comparisons
make you see things in a new way.*

# Pecos Bill Rides a Tornado

by Wyatt Blassingame

"There's a horse named Widow-
Maker, and he can't be rode.
"Every cowboy that tries is sure
to be throwed."

That's the way the song was at first. Texas
cowboys sang it while they tended their herds.
Then one starry night a cowboy named Pecos Bill
came riding through the country.

He heard the song, and he started to laugh.
"You've got that wrong," he told the other cowboys.
Bill leaned back in his saddle and sang.

> "There's not a horse that can't
>   be rode,
> "Because I'm a cowboy who can't
>   be throwed."

With that Pecos Bill got off his own horse. He
took a big leap, and he landed on Widow-Maker's
back. Widow-Maker began to buck. He jumped so
high that Bill's hat was left hanging on the moon.
He spun like a top, backflipped, and went
sidewinding up hills and down valleys, but he
couldn't throw Pecos Bill.

Finally Widow-Maker stopped bucking. He became as peaceful as a lamb and as tame as a lapdog. He became Bill's favorite horse. After that everybody knew that Pecos Bill was the best cowboy in all the West.

"Bill can ride anything with four hoofs and a hide," the other cowboys said, but nobody ever thought that Bill would have to ride a tornado. This is the way that it happened.

One spring day Bill heard about a big storm that was roaring in from the west. Lightning flashed, and thunder rolled. The rain came down like a river standing on end.

Now about that same time, he watched another storm come up from the south. The wind blew one thousand and two miles an hour. The lightning was so bright that cowboys all the way from Texas to Wyoming could see it.

Halfway between the West and the South, these two storms ran together. They met head on. They began to chase one another around and around. They turned into the biggest tornado anybody had ever seen. The tornado was so high its top kept pushing the sky out of place. Its bottom dug the Grand Canyon.

This tornado kept on roaring and leapfrogging all over the West. Bill heard that it picked up a thousand head of cattle on the Heart Bar Ranch in Texas. It put them down nice as you please on the Crooked S Ranch in Arizona. Then it picked up the cattle on the Crooked S and put them down on the Bent W Ranch in Kansas. It picked up the state of Oklahoma and put it down in New Mexico. Then it put New Mexico where Oklahoma had been.

All this was bad enough, but then the tornado made a mistake. It came roaring up the Pecos River in Texas, right past Pecos Bill's house.

Pecos Bill wasn't home when the tornado passed. He was driving some cattle to market, but he soon came riding back. "Whoa, Widow-Maker!" Pecos Bill shouted. He stopped to look around.

There stood Slue-Foot Sue, Bill's pretty wife, but there wasn't any ranchhouse. There wasn't any barn. There weren't any cottonwood trees along the Pecos River. There wasn't even any Pecos River.

"Sue," Bill shouted, "what has happened around here? Where's our Pecos River?"

"The tornado took it," said Sue.

"Where's our house and barn and cottonwood trees?" Bill asked.

"The tornado took them, too," Sue said.

That made Pecos Bill mad. "I've been driving cattle for a long time," he said. "I'm hungry. Now I come home, and some crazy tornado has stolen my house—the kitchen and all. Which way did it go?"

"That way," Sue said, pointing west, "but you can't catch it. It was traveling a thousand and two miles an hour."

"Well, it better not let me catch it," Bill said. "No tornado is going to take my house and get away with it. Get up, Widow-Maker!"

Bill galloped west. He rushed straight across Texas. He was racing over the mountains when he ran into a twenty-foot rattlesnake. The snake stood on its tail to block the way.

"You're in a mighty big hurry," the rattlesnake said.

Pecos Bill was surprised to hear a rattlesnake talk, but he was in too big a hurry to ask about it.

"Did you see a tornado come past here?" he asked the snake. "It was carrying a house and a barn and some cottonwood trees and the Pecos River."

"I did," the rattlesnake said.

"Which way did it go?"

"I won't tell, unless you can make me," the rattlesnake said. "I'm twenty feet long. I'm mean, and I'm bad, and I'm ready to fight."

Pecos Bill got down from Widow-Maker's back. "All right," he said. "I'm in a hurry. So to make it a fair fight, I'll give you the first three bites."

The rattlesnake bit Pecos Bill once. It turned gray and began to look sick. It bit Bill again, and it turned green. The rattles on its tail started to fall off. "That's enough," the rattlesnake said. "I don't want to fight." It pointed its head toward the north. "Your tornado went that way."

Bill jumped on Widow-Maker and galloped north. They rushed over more mountains and more prairies. They were racing through some high mountains when a huge mountain lion jumped down on the trail.

"You're in a mighty big hurry," the mountain lion said to Pecos Bill.

This time Bill wasn't even surprised. "I'm chasing a tornado," he shouted. "It took my house and barn and some cottonwood trees and the Pecos River. Have you seen it?"

"I have," the mountain lion said.

"Which way did it go?"

"I won't tell unless you make me," the mountain lion said. "I weigh five hundred pounds. I'm mean, and I'm bad, and I'm ready to fight."

"I don't have time to fight," Bill said. He leaned over, and he grabbed that mountain lion by the tail. He began to swing it around his head like a lasso.

"Put me down!" yelled the lion. "I'll tell you which way the tornado went."

Bill put the lion down. "Which way?" he asked.

"That way," the lion said, "but I think I hear it coming back."

Sure enough, when Bill looked up, he saw the tornado rushing toward them. It was leapfrogging from one mountain to another, turning them upside down. It was turning rivers around so they would run upstream. Lightning was flashing in eighty-two directions.

Quickly Bill took his lasso and began to spin it around and around his head. It was the longest lasso in the world. The noose got bigger and bigger, and the line got longer and longer as Bill swung it.

Then he let the noose go. It went up and up. It slipped along the bottom of the sky and over the top of the tornado.

Not even Pecos Bill could stop that tornado, but he held onto his lasso. It pulled him high in the air. It swung him back and forth like the tail of a kite.

This didn't worry Bill. Hand over hand, he climbed up the lasso.

He swung himself on the tornado's back. He began to ride it like a wild horse.

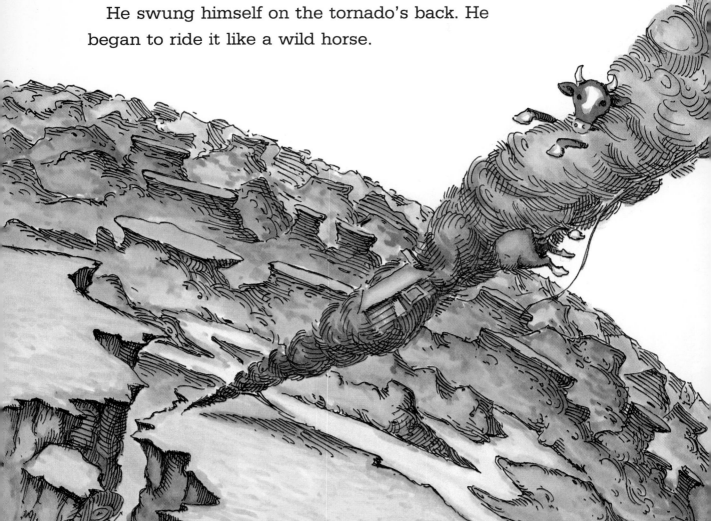

"Whoopee!" Bill yelled, waving his hat with one hand. "Buck, you crazy tornado!"

Well, that tornado really went wild. It backflipped and turned head over heels. It went sidewinding over mountains and down valleys. It sent lightning off in one hundred eighty-two directions, but it couldn't throw Pecos Bill.

Bill sat there, hitting the tornado with his hat and kicking it with his heels. Then he began to sing.

"This tornado doesn't want to
　be rode,
"But Old Pecos Bill, he can't
　be throwed."

Finally the tornado began to get tired. It got weaker and weaker. Bill made it put the cattle from the Heart Bar and the Crooked S and the Bent W ranches back where they came from. He made it put Oklahoma back below Kansas, and New Mexico back next to Arizona.

Then he made it carry his house and his barn and the cottonwood trees and the Pecos River back to Texas.

By now the tornado was so tired, it just had strength for one last bolt of lightning. Bill grabbed the lightning bolt and slid down it to the ground.

Slue-Foot Sue and Widow-Maker were waiting in front of the house.

"You've got our house and barn back," Sue said, "but what took you so long?"

"Sue," Pecos Bill said, "I've been fighting with a rattlesnake and a mountain lion. I've been riding the tornado from Oklahoma to New Mexico to Texas. Now I'm too hungry to answer questions. I want my supper."

"All right," Sue said. While she was cooking, she heard a noise outside. "What's that?" she asked Pecos Bill.

Bill looked out the window.

"It's that tornado," he said, "but now it's settled down to no more than a spring breeze. It's playing in our yard like a puppy."

"Well, let's keep it," Sue said. "It'll be nice to have a breeze of our own when the weather gets hot this summer."

## Meet a Reader

"I would need to see it to believe it," said José Guadalupe Zavala when he finished reading about Pecos Bill. José, who is eight years old, didn't believe many of the things that happened in *Pecos Bill Rides a Tornado*. However, he liked the story very much.

José, a third-grader in Illinois, has become a very good reader in English during the last year. Until he was in second grade, he went to a school in his neighborhood where only Spanish was spoken. He worked very hard to learn to read books in English. He can now take out books in both Spanish and English from the public library near his home.

José's favorite books are about cowboys. He has also read *Pecos Bill and the Wonderful Clothesline Snake* by the same author. In that story, Pecos Bill meets hoop snakes, saddle snakes, rattle snakes, glass snakes, bell snakes, and pancake snakes. Which did he like best? "The glass snake," said José, "because it broke into many pieces and then put itself back together again."

1. Tell about four things that happen when a tornado carries off Bill's ranch.
2. What does the way Bill tames Widow-Maker tell you about the kind of person Bill is?
3. Give three examples of things Bill does that make him an amazing man.
- 4. What is Bill compared to in this sentence? "The tornado swung Bill back and forth like the tail of a kite"?
- 5. How do each of the things compared help you see something in a new way?

*See your Thinker's Handbook for tips.*

- Literary Skill: Similes and metaphors

## Talk

Pick two more animals that Bill might have met. Imagine what each animal would say when Bill asked if the tornado went by. Then choose a partner and role-play the parts with one another.

Speaking/Listening: Role-playing

## Write

Write the conversation between Bill and one of the animals you chose above. Help your classmates put on a play using everyone's script.

Writing Fluency: Conversation

# Go Wind

by Lilian Moore

Go wind, blow
Push wind, swoosh.
    Shake things
    take things
    make things
       fly.

    Ring things
    swing things
    fling things
       high.

Go wind, blow
Push things——whee.
    No, wind, no.
    Not me—
    not *me*.

# Using Sense and Consonants

"Mr. Mouse and Mr. Monkey, are you ready to play the quiz game *Name That Word?* Watch the screen for your first word."

The tr__ff__c was so bad, I couldn't get home.

Okay. What's the secret word? If you're not sure, can you think of a word that makes sense? Try these words: *weather, road, traffic, terrific.*

Yes, my friends, you are right when you say that the first three words make sense in the sentence. Which of the words has the same consonants as tr__ff__c? The words *traffic* and *terrific* have almost the same consonants, but only *traffic* had the same consonants as tr__ff__c *and* makes sense in the sentence.

When you read and come to a word you don't know, read the whole sentence and then think of a word that makes sense. Then see if the consonants in your word are the same as the consonants in the new word.

What word goes in the next sentence: *dripping, dropping, driving?*

I kept dr__pp__ng the ball.

*Dropping* and *dripping* have the same consonants, but does *dripping* make sense? No. The word that makes sense and has the same consonants is *dropping.*

### Practicing Using Sense and Consonants

Now read the underlined words in the sentences. Use sense and the consonants to help you.

1. The racer handed the <u>baton</u>, a long hollow tube, to the next runner.
2. A <u>sprint</u> is a race that is run at full speed.

### Tips for Understanding Sense and Consonants

• Use sense and consonants to help you figure out new words you don't know.
• Read the whole sentence and think of a word that would make sense in the sentence.
• See if the consonants in your word are the same as those in the new word.
• For other tips on figuring out words, see your Word Study Handbook.

*For Ron, getting there means becoming a track star. Read to find out if Ron has what it takes to "get there." As you read, notice how many events all come under the sport of track.*

# Track Is for Me

by Lowell A. Dickmeyer

   Hi! I'm Ron. I want to be a track star. That's not such a crazy idea, because I come from a track-minded family. My dad was once a mile runner in college. Casey, my older brother, is a long jumper at the University of California. And my sister Lela is a sprinter, or short-distance runner, at her high school.

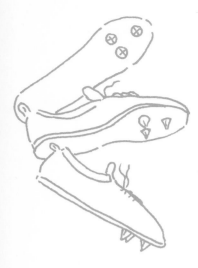

"Track" is a short name for the sport of track and field. The sport is really made up of many different kinds of competitions. There are running, jumping, and throwing events.

I have always liked to run, and I am pretty good at throwing and jumping too. So when I became ten years old, I joined the Panthers track team. It has special classes for different age groups. We compete with children our own age from other city track teams.

Before I joined the Panthers team, I had to go to a doctor for a checkup. He signed a paper saying I was healthy.

**Spikes** are special track shoes with metal points sticking out of the soles. These points bite into the ground to prevent slipping and sliding.

Panthers had to buy their own running shoes. My first pair had rippled rubber bottoms, but I soon started wearing **spikes** too. Younger runners and persons just starting out in track do not wear spikes because they might hurt themselves on the sharp points.

The Panthers practiced at a nearby high school. Coach Davis began each practice with a time to warm up. We did bends. We stretched. We touched our toes. We did exercises, like push-ups and sit-ups. But most of all, we ran. "Running," Coach Davis said, "is the starting point of track."

We worked out on a big cinder path called a **track.** It was 440 yards around. The track was marked off into lanes by white lines. During races, runners start in different lanes. Short-distance runners, or sprinters, cannot step out of their lanes for a whole race. Long-distance runners can cross over in the inside lanes during a race.

**Did You Know?**
A **track** is an oval-shaped cinder path that is one quarter mile long from start to finish.

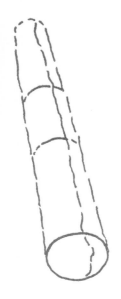

The Panthers practiced for two weeks before our first meet. At meets, each of us could compete in as many as four different events. That meant that at practices, we had to spend time learning the special skills needed for several running, jumping, and throwing events.

I soon learned that there is a lot more to running a race than you might think. In the first place, there are four different kinds of races. There are sprints, longer distances, hurdles, and relays. Each kind of race takes special running skills. Coach Davis showed us what we needed to know for each race.

Sprinters get a faster start by using starting blocks. Very fast starts are not as important in distance races because you have more time to make up for a bad start. Distance runners set a slower **pace.**

**pace,** a runner's rate or speed.

Running hurdles takes a different kind of skill. Hurdles are really small fences blocking the lanes of a track. Good runners don't jump over hurdles. They lean forward and stretch their legs. You have to be careful not to hook a hurdle with your trailing foot.

Relay races are not like other races in which one person runs the whole race. In a relay race, a team of four people splits up the distances into four parts called **legs.** Each person runs one leg. The runners in a relay carry a **baton.**

**baton,** a hollow tube that is passed from one runner to the next in a relay.

When a runner finishes a leg, he or she must pass the baton to the next runner. The worst thing you can do in a relay race is drop the baton. That is why

Coach Davis had us practice the baton pass over and over again.

After learning about the different running events, I decided to enter three at our first track meet. They would be the 100-yard sprint, the 440-yard run, and the 440-yard relay. I picked the long jump for my field event.

The long jump takes both running and jumping skills. It is important to reach full speed on the run before the jump. You should keep an even **stride.** My brother Casey showed me how to use markers to help me measure my stride. My markers were pieces of wood. I set them along the runway.

**stride,** runners use short or long steps or strides for different events. Figuring out the best stride comes with practice.

**take-off board,** the board from which the jumper begins a jump.

**foul,** do something against the rules of the race.

If I did it right, my last step would hit the **take-off board** just right. I wouldn't step beyond it and **foul** out.

Just before reaching the take-off board, I started lowering my body a little. Casey said I should feel like a cat getting ready to spring. My last step came down hard on the take-off board. I straightened my knee and leaped into the air.

While in the air, I folded in the middle and snapped my legs and arms forward. I landed in the sand, heels first. I fell forward so that no part of my body would touch the sand behind my heel marks. You can lose inches on your jump by falling backward when you land.

At each practice, I felt myself getting better. I looked forward to my first track meet. The Panthers would be against the Westlake Hawks.

At the last practice before the meet, Coach Davis said, "Eat lightly before a meet. Don't fill up with water or soft drinks before you race. You might get cramps. Don't chew gum. You might choke. Try to think of yourself as panthers. The fastest panthers are hungry panthers."

I was scared as I got ready for my first race, the 100-yard dash. I picked up some starting blocks and went to my lane.

The person who starts the race came over and talked to us. He told us not to jump the gun. If someone got a head start, the race would have to start over again. Anyone who jumped the gun two times would foul out.

We went back into our lanes and planted our feet into our blocks. "On your marks! Get set!"

**Bang!**

I pushed out of the blocks as hard as I could. I picked up speed. I tried to remember to move in a straight line. I kept my eyes and toes pointed ahead. My arms were swinging back and forth at my sides. I ran on the balls of my feet and lifted my knees high to make my stride longer.

Suddenly I felt my nails digging into my hands. "Take it easy," I told myself. I loosened my hands. That helped.

I crossed the finish line at top speed. But top speed wasn't good enough. I came in fourth. And fourth place didn't win any points for the Panthers. I was disappointed, but I remembered to be a good sport. I went over to the winner and shook his hand.

Later that morning, I ran the 440-yard run. This time I came in third. I earned my first point for the Panthers. It was a great feeling.

On my way to the long jump, I saw Carlos get ready for the shot put. He stood in the throwing circle with his back to the throwing field. Carlos held the shot in his right hand. He carried it with the tips of his fingers. Then he tucked the shot next to his neck. Suddenly he bent forward on one leg. As Carlos shoved the shot outward, he straightened his arm and body at the same time. The shot sailed through the air. Carlos danced a little on his right foot to keep his balance. He did not step out of the throwing circle. The judges marked the spot where the shot made a dent in the grass. Carlos smiled at me. He seemed pleased. I sure was. It was a good put.

20

15

10

Now it was time for my long jump. I started forward and got into my stride. I soared out over the sand. It was a good jump. I felt it.

I had two more tries to better my first jump. But the first was my best one. I took second place and won three points.

As the day went on, the track meet was "nip and tuck." The Panthers would have to place first in the last two events to win.

The Panthers' best runner, Janey, was running in the girls' half-mile race. Coach Davis told Janey to stick to her own pace.

"Don't fall into the habit of being a 'rabbit,'" said Coach Davis. "Sometimes fast runners do not save enough energy for a strong finish. If you run like they do, you might burn yourself out."

As the gun sounded, the girls raced down the track. Halfway through the race, Janey was still behind the lead runner. I wondered if she was fast enough to win. But then in the final stretch, Janey put out everything she had. With a burst of speed, she ran past the Westlake runner. Janey broke the tape to win.

The 440-yard relay was the only event left. I was running the third leg. I went to my place halfway around the track. Soon the starting gun cracked on the other side of the field. Two sprinters raced side by side into the first turn. I saw the batons flashing in their hands as they pumped their arms up and down to pick up speed. In no time at all, they were making their first pass.

We were getting close to the end of the second passing zone. I still did not feel the baton. Then Red Murphy slapped the baton into my hand. I wrapped my fingers around it. Now I just had to run as fast as I could.

Sammy, our **anchor man,** or the last runner in the relay, was waiting for me. My lungs were burning. The Westlake runner was taking the lead. Sammy was going so fast that I was afraid I wouldn't be able to get the baton to him. I was out of breath. Sammy did slow down enough for me to slap the baton into his hand. Then he took off down the final leg.

When I got to the finish line, I found out that Westlake had won. The Panthers had lost the meet.

Even though we lost, it had been a wonderful day. Each of us won at least one ribbon for placing in different events. My family and friends were proud of me. I was on my way to becoming a track star!

*For some people, getting there is not the most enjoyable part of the trip. For the disabled, getting there can be the hardest thing to do. As you read pages from Rachel's journal see how she solves the problem of "getting there." Think about what a building must have for disabled people to use it easily.*

# Rachel's Journal

by Rachel Hitch

March 3

Hope's Hobby Shop just opened down the street. It's a neat place. It has all the latest models and kits. Mr. Hope, the owner, lets the kids build models right in the store. He has a work bench with tools along the back wall of the shop.

All the kids go there after school. Mike made an airplane that really flies. Ann made a robot from a kit. Jake is making a model of the *Columbia Space Shuttle.* It sounds like fun.

I wish I could go there, but there are two steps down into the shop. My wheelchair can't go down the stairs. There's no ramp. There is no way that I can get into the building.

All my friends go to the hobby shop. Because it doesn't have a ramp, I can't go. I'm angry.

March 4

I was talking to my friend Jake today. We are in the same class at school. I told him about wanting to go to Hope's Hobby Shop. He's going to talk to Mr. Hope. Jake believes Mr. Hope has just not thought about needing a ramp. He may need someone to remind him.

Jake saw Mr. Hope today. It didn't go well. Mr. Hope said, "I don't have time to worry about a ramp. My job is to run the store, not wait on one disabled kid. Besides, I don't own the building."

Mr. Hope told Jake that the owner of the whole building is a Mr. Green. He told Jake to talk to him. I think I will see Mr. Green myself.

March 6

Today I explained to Mr. Green that the hobby shop in his building cannot be used by people in wheelchairs. I asked him to add a ramp so that disabled people could use his building.

He said he understood my problem, although he would not put in a ramp just for one person. He patted me on the head and told me to go home.

Mr. Green may think he doesn't have to put in a ramp, but he hasn't heard the last about needing to have buildings open for *all* people to use.

I'm not sure what to do next, but I'm thinking. Somehow I am going to get into that hobby shop. I'm going to build a wonderful robot.

March 13

My teacher, Ms. Rose, asked me to stay after class. She could see I was discouraged about something. I told her about the meetings with Mr. Hope and Mr. Green.

Ms. Rose says we should not give up the fight. She thinks we are working for something important and has promised to help.

The next day Ms. Rose called a class meeting so we could discuss the problem. Lucy said we should put on a class play. Other children joined in and gave ideas. The play could show what it's like to be disabled and left out of things everyone else can do. We started work right away.

We will invite Mr. Hope and Mr. Green. They will be surprised to see a play about them. The stage is set to look just like the hobby shop. It even has two steps. Jake plays Mr. Green. Mike plays Mr. Hope. I am playing myself. The rest of the class will be children working in the shop.

March 17

We did the play last night. It was a big hit. Mr. Green said he had not understood before how making the hobby shop open to everyone was so important to all of us. But he understands now. He also thought Jake did a good job of playing him.

Mr. Green said, "That was quite a play. You did help me to see this problem in a new way, but I will not build a ramp!"

We all felt angry and surprised when he said that. Then Mr. Green said, "I *will* buy what you need to build the ramp yourselves. Mr. Hope and I will help." We all cheered.

There are still many buildings without ramps, but change is coming. More people now can see that everyone should be able to enter a building even if he or she is disabled.

I guess I'll think about all the buildings that don't have ramps tomorrow. Today I am really happy about the new ramp at Hope's Hobby Shop.

# Comprehension Check

1. Do you think Ron has what it takes to become a track star? Tell why you think as you do.
2. Would you call Ron a "good sport"? Why?
3. In the selection "Rachel's Journal," what is Rachel's problem and how is it solved?
4. What are things a building has to have if it is to be used easily by disabled people?
• 5. What is the connecting word in each sentence? Tell what two ideas the words connect.
   a. I was disappointed, but I was a good sport.
   b. He won't put in a ramp, although he says he understands the problem.

• Comprehension Skill: Connecting words

# Communication Workshop

*Talk*

With a group of classmates, discuss reasons people might have to keep a journal. Does anyone in the group keep a journal for a special reason?

Speaking/Listening: Cooperative learning

*Write*

Take one of the ways to use a journal that you talked about above and write one day's entry. Share your entry with a friend.

Writing Fluency: Journal entry

# Using a Table of Contents

Lily spent all day riding around town on her bike, trying to find the library. She had no map and she didn't ask for directions. Having a map or asking someone who lives in town could have saved her a lot of time.

Just as maps and directions help you get where you are going, a **table of contents** helps you get where you're going when you read.

A **table of contents** is a list that tells you what is in a book. Here is how to use it.

1. Look for it at the beginning of the book.
2. Look down the list of selection titles until you find the one you want.
3. Look at the number. It tells you the page where the selection begins.

Find the Table of Contents in this book. Look up the story "Yertle the Turtle." On what page does it begin?

*Not so long ago, only a few people believed we could travel easily into space and return to earth. The space shuttle has changed all that. As you read the next selection, ask yourself how the shuttle is helping us learn to live in space.*

# High Road to Space

by Kay Garvin

Before people sailed the oceans, they dreamed of travel to other worlds. Almost two thousand years ago, a man named Lucian wrote a story about a trip to the moon. Hundreds of years later, writers and artists gave us stories and pictures of strange and wonderful worlds beyond our galaxy.

Some of their ideas seem funny today. Some ideas were plainly wrong. Once, not so long ago, people talked of the streams on the planet Mars. We know now that Mars is a nearly dry planet.

Travel Through Space: An Everyday Idea

Today, the idea of space travel is no longer just a dream. Someday soon, traveling through space may become an everyday job for some people, just as flying airplanes is an everyday job today.

The space shuttle has helped more people believe in the idea of travel through space. Before the space shuttle, rockets could be used only once to get into space. These rockets were very costly. The **space shuttle** is a ship that we can use again and again to get into space.

A shuttle uses rockets to take off, but they, like the shuttle, can be used for more than one trip. Once the shuttle is in flight, the rockets drop away and are picked up in the ocean for reuse. The shuttle returns to Earth safely without them. When people see the shuttle land as smoothly as an airplane, they can believe that we now have a safer and less costly way of getting into space.

A space shuttle, though, is not a spaceship, because it can't fight the pull of the earth and travel far past the moon. It is better to think of the shuttle as a kind of "space truck." Like trucks on earth, the shuttle helps people move things from one place to another.

The things that a shuttle carries are called its **payload.** A payload might be anything that scientists want to learn more about.

## The Crew on a Space Shuttle

People are needed to take care of the payloads on any shuttle **mission.** The first shuttle missions carried a **crew** of three people. Now the shuttle can carry as many as seven people.

Each person has a special job. The **commander** is like the captain of a ship. He or she is in charge of the whole mission. The **pilot** takes over when the shuttle is leaving the earth or landing. At that time, the commander acts as the copilot. A third person on the crew is the **mission specialist.** This person sees that all jobs are done safely and on time. Like the commander and the pilot, the mission specialist is trained as an **astronaut.**

The other four people who might travel on a shuttle are called **payload specialists.** They are almost always scientists. They carry out experiments. They are not trained as astronauts. Still, they must be able to do every job on the shuttle in case of emergencies.

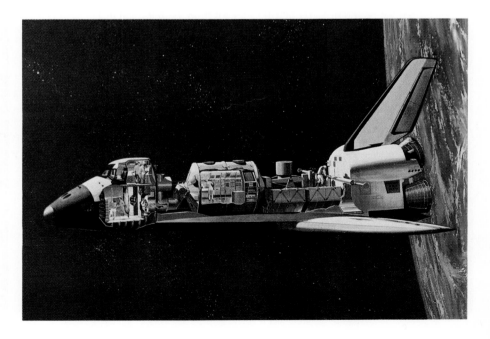

## Computers and the Shuttle

There could be no space flight without computers. The crew of a shuttle trains with computers. Computers give a crew problems to solve. These problems are like those that might come up during a flight. By solving these problems, the crew can get a preview of what it will be like 690 miles above the earth.

Five computers on board do the most important jobs on the shuttle. They make sure that every part of the ship is safe before the shuttle takes off. They start the engines at exactly, the right times. Even when the pilot is in charge, a computer tells him or her what to do.

When you're traveling at 17,000 miles an hour, you can misjudge what is happening. That's why computers are so important to the crew. Computers can use facts to decide about things much faster than we can with our minds.

**Did You Know?**
After the shuttle takes off, several computers keep track of everything that happens. By pressing some buttons, the pilot can get a quick answer to almost any question.

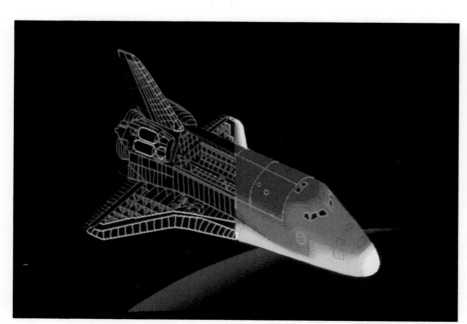

A computer shows how the shuttle heats up when it comes back to Earth. The hottest parts of the shuttle are white, and the coolest parts are purple.

### On Board the Space Shuttle

What's it like to travel on board a space shuttle? The air is like the air we breathe on earth. But several things are different.

Probably the first thing you would notice is that you seem to be heavier as the shuttle leaves the ground. Your weight on earth doesn't change, but the pull of the earth as the shuttle takes off makes you weigh about three times as much as you do at home. That lasts for several minutes. Hundreds of miles above the earth, you would weigh almost nothing!

When you weigh almost nothing, you become **weightless.** This means you could float around the shuttle. You could even stand on your head for hours. Maybe that sounds like fun, but some of the astronauts would disagree. Tossing about on a space-ship is like tossing about on a ship on a stormy ocean. Many astronauts are sick during the first few hours of flight. Many enjoy weightlessness after that.

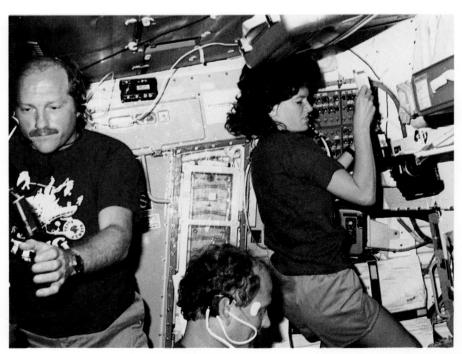

## Life on a Shuttle

Other things on a space shuttle are different from being on the ground. For example, even though you can choose from more than a hundred different foods in the shuttle's tiny kitchen, most of these foods are dried. To make the eggs, fruit, fish, or anything else taste as it would on earth, you have to add water. Then you have to take care that your weightless food doesn't float away.

Life on a shuttle is not always very comfortable. However, many people believe that what we can do and learn in space is worth an uncomfortable trip.

**Did You Know?**
Water that is spilled on board a shuttle does not drip down. Instead, it floats in the air in the shape of little balls.

*Space shuttles will do much more than help us travel through space. Read to find out about the important work the space shuttles will do for us.*

# Those Hard-working Shuttles

by Roger Mills

Until 1980, the only way to get a satellite into place in the skies was to send it up on a rocket. Each rocket cost a lot of money, and a rocket was good for only one trip. If the satellite didn't do its job, there was no way to fix it. There just had to be a better way of sending up satellites.

## The Space Shuttle

The space shuttle gave us a better way of learning more about space. For the first time ever, we could put satellites in space and return to earth safely. It costs more to send up a shuttle than it does to send up a rocket, but a shuttle can do much more than a rocket.

A shuttle can be used again and again. It can fly many trips before it wears out. On one of those trips its crew might set loose a new satellite one day and repair an old satellite the next day. Someone from the shuttle might float out to fix the satellite, or the crew might bring the satellite inside.

A shuttle can carry 65,000 pounds of payload. The really big payload fits into what is called the **cargo bay.** This part of the shuttle is big enough to carry a bus. Some payloads, like *Spacelab,* stay in the cargo bay. Others, like the *Space Telescope,* are set loose. Some people say that someday we will be able to build cities in space. If that is so, many heavy things will have to be carried into space. That day could never come without the hard-working shuttles.

Use what you know about watching for special type to get more out of what you read.

### The Shuttle's *Spacelab*

How do our hearts beat when we weigh nothing at all? In the shuttle's *Spacelab,* specialists work to find the answer. They do experiments with animals to see how they act when weightless.

The work done in *Spacelab* will give scientists answers to hundreds of different questions. It will also help them do new kinds of work. One shuttle carried an experiment in mixing metals that could not be mixed on earth. Another made a special kind of medicine that could not be made here. Other specialists will study the sun and the storms that blow across it.

## The *Space Telescope*

We know the air around the earth is not very clean. The space shuttle won't make it any cleaner, but it will help some of us get above it. That's why people who study the stars are excited about the *Space Telescope*. The shuttle soon will put this telescope into space.

A **telescope** here on earth lets us see to the edges of our galaxy. The *Space Telescope,* though, will circle the earth at 22,500 miles. It will gather light traveling through empty space. We can see much better through light that is gathered in empty space than through light that travels through dusty, smoky air. In its high place above the earth, the *Space Telescope* will help us see farther and more clearly than ever before.

**telescope,** instrument that makes far away objects appear nearer.

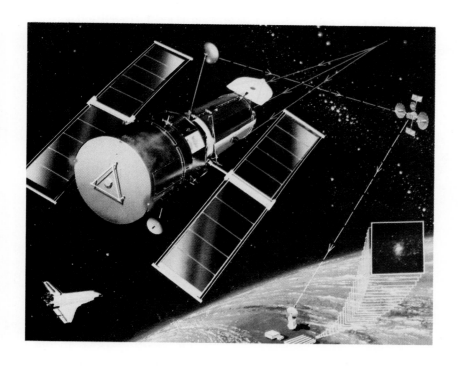

### The Space Shuttle and You

The space shuttle will help us answer many big questions, but that doesn't mean it can't do small jobs. Suppose you have a good idea for an experiment to be done in space. Your school can ask NASA to carry your experiment on one of the shuttle's trips. **NASA** is the special office that plans our country's space trips. It chooses about 25 such experiments a year. One school sent 10,000 ants into space. Another wanted to know how bees would act far above the earth.

Your school will not have to pay if your experiment is chosen. Other people pay about 3,000 dollars to put their experiments on the shuttle.

NASA has certain rules for *all* small experiments. They must fit into a small space. They must be safe. They must not take up more time than it takes to turn them on and off. Unless your experiment meets these rules, it won't go on board.

## Future Work of the Space Shuttles

Future shuttles will carry more satellites that will watch the earth. These satellites will be able to see things on earth that can be seen only from space.

Thanks to satellites that are already in space, we can see where rivers run under the ground. We can see how more and more parts of the world are becoming very dry land. We can tell how the forests and oceans are changing.

What will the weather be like in the next few months? Are the farmers of the world going to have a good year? The satellites taken into space by the hard-working shuttles will give us the answer.

## INDEX

**Think and Discuss**

1. How will the space shuttle help us learn about living in space?
2. Name two other important things the shuttle can do.
3. If you could choose an experiment to be carried on a future shuttle mission, what would it be? Why?
- 4. If you wanted to know what kind of experiments are done on board a space shuttle, which entry of the Index on page 239 would help?
- 5. Use the Index to figure out which pages tell you about payloads.
- Study Skill: Index

# Communication Workshop

**Talk**

There are good and bad things about living on a shuttle. Do you think there are more good things than bad? Discuss the pros and cons with a partner.

Speaking/Listening: Discussion

**Write**

Make two lists that show the good and bad points about life on a shuttle. At the bottom of the page, tell whether you would like to go on one. Compare your lists with your partner's.

Writing Fluency: Lists

# LOOKING BACK

**Thinking and Writing About the Section**

See your Thinker's Handbook for tips.

**Prewriting**

Some interesting characters showed up in Section Four, "Getting There." You can write about one of them in a descriptive paragraph to share with your family. Copy the chart and fill it in.

|  | Pecos Bill | Ron | Rachel | Shuttle Crews |
|---|---|---|---|---|
| How do they act? | bigger than life |  |  |  |
| How do they feel? |  |  | determined |  |
| How do they look? |  |  |  | cramped like sardines |

**Writing**

Write a descriptive paragraph about one of the characters in the chart. Include details and use one simile or metaphor to describe the person. See your Writer's Handbook if you need more help.

**Revising**

Read your first draft to a partner. Does your topic sentence tell who you are describing? Is your description vivid? Did you use a simile or metaphor? Make changes, proofread, and write a final copy.

**Presenting**

Share your paragraph with your family.

# 5

# Growing

**MOM:** You're *too old* for this.

**DAD:** You're *not old enough* for that.

**TEACHER:** Class, start acting *more grown up.*

Growing up isn't always fun or easy. Growing doesn't seem to end. As long as you live, you'll never stop learning and growing. In this section, you'll read about people growing up and learning about friends and families. As you read, think of how you're growing this year.

# Statements of Fact and Opinion

Suppose your family gets a new puppy. You and your sister are thinking of a name. Just then your neighbor comes over and says, "Too bad. Your puppy is not nearly as cute as mine."

Don't get upset! What your neighbor told you is her *opinion*. It is not a *fact!*

A **statement of fact** can be proved to be true or false. A **statement of opinion** tells you what someone thinks or believes. You probably think your puppy is the cutest puppy ever. That is your opinion. Your neighbor has his opinion. There is no way to prove which puppy is cuter. Words like *cute, best, should,* and *beautiful* are often clues that tell you a statement of opinion is being given.

When you read, it is important to be able to tell the difference between a statement of fact and a statement of opinion. You can check facts in books, see something with your own eyes, or check with someone who knows. You don't have to check every statement of fact, you just need to know that it can be checked. Statements of opinion may be explained, but there is no real way to check them.

Think about what you know about facts and opinions as you read about Kitty O'Neil.

Deaf people should try many things. Kitty O'Neil has been deaf since she was a baby. As Kitty grew up, her mother let her try many different things. Kitty O'Neil has won medals in swimming and diving.

**1.** Is the first sentence a statement of fact or opinion?

It is a statement of opinion. You cannot prove it. The word *should* is a clue to an opinion.

**2.** Is the second sentence a statement of fact or opinion?

Did you say that it is a statement of fact because the answer can be checked? It can be checked by asking Kitty or her mother.

## Practicing Finding Facts and Opinions

Read some more information about Kitty O'Neil.

Today, Kitty O'Neil has a wonderful job. She does stunts for TV shows. One time Kitty O'Neil jumped from an airplane without a parachute. She landed on an airbag. Kitty is also a fine racing car driver who likes setting speed records. Kitty O'Neil has not let being deaf stop her from doing many exciting things. This way of looking at herself has helped Kitty grow up to have a job she likes to do.

1. Which of these is a statement of fact?
   a. Today, O'Neil has a wonderful job.
   b. She does stunts for TV shows.
2. Explain why you picked the answer you did.
3. Which of these is a statement of opinion?
   a. O'Neil jumped from an airplane.
   b. O'Neil is a fine racing car driver.
4. Explain why you picked the answer you did.

## Tips for Reading on Your Own

- To decide if a statement is fact or if it is opinion, ask yourself if it can be proved to be true or false. If it can be proved, it's a statement of fact. If it cannot be proved, it's a statement of opinion.
- To check a statement of fact, ask yourself if you can look it up, ask someone, or see it yourself.
- Are there words that give you clues to a statement of opinion?

*Do you feel old? Do you feel young? Whether you are truly old or young may depend on whether you are a person or a mayfly. Read to find out why it's hard to know the meaning of words such as* old *and* young. *As you read, look for statements of fact and statements of opinion.*

# Old, Older, Oldest

by Leonore Klein

Who is old?
Are you old?
Or are you young?

Is "old" when your bones feel achy and cold? If it is, then Michael, who is eight, is old. Michael has the flu. He feels achy and cold all over. Even his toes feel achy. And his eyelashes feel cold.

Is "young" when you kick up your heels and dance?

Then Grandma, who is sixty-five, is young.

"You're as young as you feel," says Grandma. "And I feel like dancing."

What is really old? Is sixty-five old? Is eight old? It's hard to say.

In the spring Michael plays near a pond. A group of Mayflies live there. They are pretty. They have delicate wings and threadlike tails.

A Mayfly starts life as a water creature called a nymph. In the late springtime it hatches into an adult Mayfly. Mayflies live for a day, or, at most, three days.

An adult Mayfly is old when it is *three days* old!

Down in the cellar of Michael's house lives a small gray mouse.

If Michael's mother knew he lived there, she would set a trap and try to catch him. But she doesn't.

This mouse is four years old, just the same age as Michael's younger sister Katy.

But this mouse is an old mouse.

He has grandchildren and great-grandchildren, and even great-great-great-great-grandchildren.

Mice don't live to be older than *four years*.

Sometimes a squirrel comes to play in the oak tree in Michael's garden. This squirrel likes to eat the acorns when they fall from the tree.

Michael and Katy don't know how old this squirrel is. They call him "Quickie," because he scampers away from them so quickly.

Michael would be surprised to know that he and this squirrel have the same birth date. They were both born eight years, four days, and six hours ago.

Michael is a young boy.

But Quickie is an old, old squirrel.

How old is old for a furry, gray squirrel?

*Eight years* is old!

Katy and Michael have a dog. Arnold Appleby, who lives next door, has a cat. Katy and Michael's dog and Arnold Appleby's cat never fight. That is because Arnold's cat is too old and too lazy to hiss or spit at a dog. She is nearly fifteen years old.

Katy and Michael's dog is one year old. He is still a puppy. He barks and barks at Arnold's cat. But Arnold's cat just sits still and looks at him.

*Cats* and *dogs* are old cats and old dogs when they are about *thirteen years* old—almost Arnold Appleby's age.

When Katy and Michael go to the zoo, they like to look at the two huge hippopotamuses. They can't tell the old hippopotamus from the young hippopotamus because the old hippopotamus and the young hippopotamus both look the same—very fat and very tough-skinned and very ugly. At least, Katy and Michael think they look ugly.

The fact of the matter is, a hippopotamus is an old hippopotamus when he is *forty years* old.

A swan is an old swan when he is *forty-five years* old.

Katy and Michael's grandma once had a swan live on the pond on her farm. He flew away one year and never came back.

Elephants live even longer than swans.

Parrots live even longer than elephants.

And people live even longer than parrots.

An elephant is old at *fifty*.

A parrot is old at *sixty-five*.

A person is old at *eighty*.

But a few people live to be over *one hundred years* old.

Katy and Michael once saw the oldest animal of all in their part of the world—in the aquarium. They saw a giant tortoise. It was 150 years old!

Giant tortoises live longer than any other animal.

Little animals can live as long as big animals. This little animal is as small as a clam. Its name is "pearl mussel," and it lives longer than a great big elephant!

The earth we live on is very, very old.

Michael isn't as old as the earth.

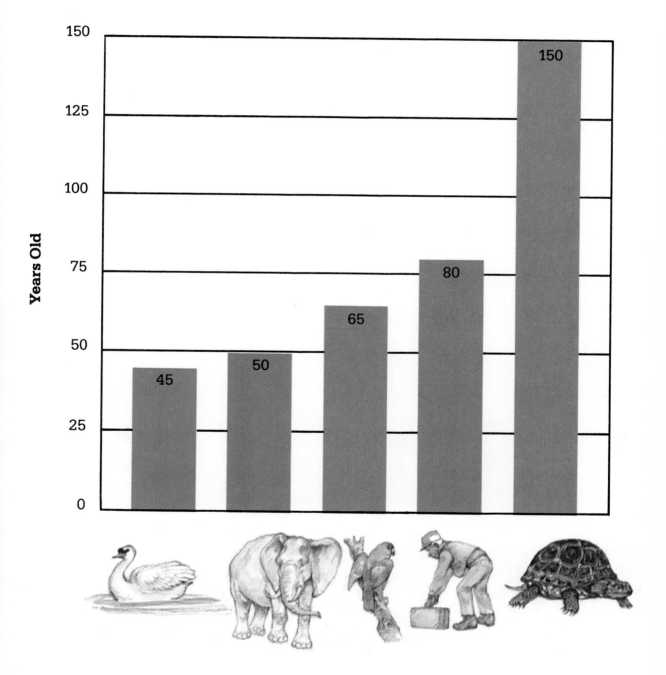

Michael, of course, is only eight. But Michael can read and write, ride a two-wheeler bike and play the piano. That's why his sister Katy, who is only four, thinks he is old. She can't read or write or ride a two-wheeler bike. She can't play the piano.

Michael doesn't think he is old, but he'd like to be. He'd like to be as old as Arnold Appleby.

Arnold Appleby goes to high school. He plays the drums in the high-school band and delivers newspapers on a motorbike. Arnold Appleby is sixteen.

He doesn't think he is old. He thinks Michael's father is old. Michael's father is thirty. Michael's mother is thirty too. Michael's father can stay up until one o'clock at night if he wants to. He shaves, has a job, and drives a car.

Michael's father doesn't think he is old. He thinks his own mother is old. His mother is Michael's grandma, and she is sixty-five. She just retired from her job and she travels a lot. "I'm getting on," Grandma says, "but my mother still thinks I'm young."

Grandma's mother is Michael's great-grandma. She is ninety. She always tells her daughter, "No matter how old you get, you'll still be my baby!"

"I do feel like a baby sometimes," says Grandma. "But other times I feel old and wise."

Some young people feel old already.

Some old people feel young.

How old are you?

Do you feel old? Do you feel young?

How old would you like to be?

## Think and Discuss

1. Why is it hard to find a meaning for words such as *old* and *young?*
2. Why can't Katy and Michael tell the young hippos from the old ones?
3. Why does Katy think Michael is old, when Michael thinks Arnold is old?
4. What does Grandma mean by saying, "I do feel like a baby sometimes, but other times I feel old and wise."
• 5. Tell if these statements are facts or opinions.
   a. You're as young as you feel.
   b. Michael's grandma retired from her job.

*See your Thinker's Handbook for tips.*

● Comprehension Skill: Fact and opinion

# Communication Workshop

## Talk

Get together with a partner. Name the people and animals in this selection and tell the age of each. Discuss if that person or animal is old or young.

Speaking/Listening: Discussion

## Write

Choose one character you named. Write a paragraph about what that person might say about feeling old or young. Read it aloud. Does any classmate with the same character express similar feelings?

Writing Fluency: Paragraph

*One of the worst parts of growing up is dealing with bullies. Emily Mott can't imagine why Johnny Ringer is always picking on her. Read to find out why Johnny won't leave Emily alone and what Emily does about it. Notice as you read how the order of events makes a difference to this selection.*

# The Origami Truce

by Christine McDonnell

Every day in September at recess Emily and Ivy liked to play games with the small pink balls you could buy at the corner store, the ones called high bouncers. Their friends played too.

"*A* my name is *Alice* and my husband's name is *Arthur* and we live in *Alabama* and we sell *Anteaters.*"

Phyllis bounced the ball in a steady rhythm, swinging her leg over every time she said an *A* word. Then she went on to the *B*'s.

"*B* my name is *Barbara* and my husband's name is *Bill* and we live in *Boston* and we sell *Baboons.*" She was trying to think of an animal for every letter in the alphabet.

Emily stood next to Patricia O'Hare, waiting for her turn. Phyllis missed on the letter *E.* She couldn't think of an *E* place.

"*Egypt,*" offered Emily. She always knew *E* because that was the letter that her own name began with.

The next one up was Patricia. Her bushy curls bounced in rhythm with the ball. She went through the letters quickly. But at *J* she couldn't think of something to sell. She gave the ball an angry bounce before she tossed it to Emily.

Emily had got up to the letter *G* when something hard hit her on the back of her neck, making her miss her next bounce.

She rubbed her neck where it stung and looked

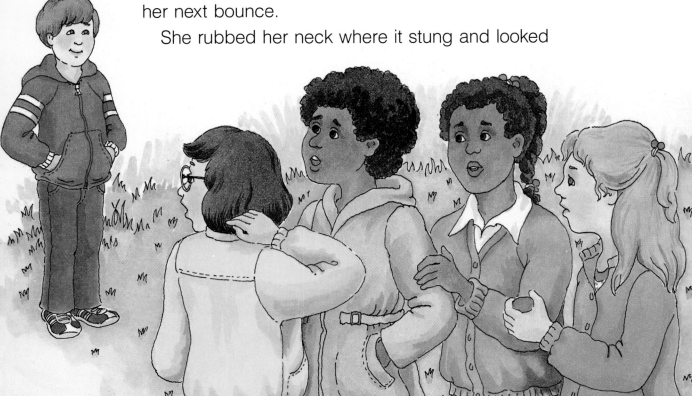

around. Not far from the circle of girls stood Johnny Ringer, grinning.

"What's the matter, Mott? Can't even bounce a ball?"

"I was doing fine until you came along."

Johnny laughed. "Made you miss, huh?"

"Yeah, you made me miss."

"See. You're not perfect, after all."

"I never said I was."

"Think you're so smart. Showoff."

Emily felt herself blush. Johnny wasn't being fair. She wasn't a showoff.

"Get lost, Ringer," said Ivy. "Find a cliff and jump off."

"Yeah," said Patricia. "You think you're so tough."

Emily didn't say anything. She looked down at the playground and kicked a pebble away. It was probably the same pebble that Johnny had thrown.

"Ah, what do you know, anyway?" said Johnny. He walked off with his hands in his pockets, trying to walk like a tough guy.

From that point on, Johnny Ringer picked on Emily at least two times a week. He put paste on her chair. He stole her spelling notebook and hid it behind the hamster cage. He wrote on her desk with a marker that wouldn't wash off.

"I don't get it," Ivy said.

"What did you ever do to him?"

Emily shrugged. She didn't know.

Finally Leo took Johnny aside. "Listen, Ringer, you're acting dumb. Emily hasn't done anything to you."

"How do you know?"

"Name one thing she's done."

"She gives me a pain. She thinks she's so smart, always winning the math relays and stuff."

Leo shook his head. "That's dumb."

"Don't call me dumb. I'm sick of people calling me that."

"Ok. But listen. Leave Emily alone."

"What'll you do if I don't?"

"You'll find out," said Leo in a low voice.

Johnny looked at him carefully but said nothing. Then with a quick dart of his fist, he punched Leo in the arm and stepped away fast.

Leo rubbed his arm and went back to his desk.

Emily looked up.

"What a jerk," Leo said, still rubbing his arm. "He doesn't like you because you're smart, Emily."

Emily brushed her bangs out of her eyes and straightened her glasses. "What?"

"That's what he said." Leo made a silly face, as if to try to cheer her up.

Emily looked across the room. Johnny stood by the hamster cage, poking his pencil between the bars.

After that, Emily tried to keep a distance between herself and Johnny. She sat far away from him at lunch and at singing. She hoped she'd never be paired with him in math. At recess she stuck with the other kids, figuring that he wouldn't bother her if she was part of a group.

Ivy tried to cheer her up. "Maybe he'll find someone else to pick on. Maybe he'll catch chicken pox or get the flu and stay out of school for a month. Maybe he'll move away."

Her ideas made Emily smile, but inside she was still worried.

Emily even tried to hide being smart a little. She stopped raising her hand when she knew the answer, and sometimes she made mistakes on purpose when she was at the board.

"Emily, that isn't like you," said Mrs. Higgenbottom. "What's the matter, dear?"

She looked so worried that Emily almost blurted out the whole problem. But she stopped herself just in time.

What could Mrs. Higgenbottom do about it, anyway? Besides, if Johnny found out, he might do something terrible. So she didn't tell Mrs. Higgenbottom after all.

One day at the beginning of October, Mrs. Higgenbottom told the class, "We're having a teacher from Japan come and visit with us for a few weeks. His name is Mr. Uchida."

Everyone began to talk at once.

"Can he speak English?"

"What does he look like?"

"What do they eat in Japan?"

"When's he coming?"

The questions blurred together in a hubbub.

"Class, simmer down. I'll answer your questions one at a time."

Mrs. Higgenbottom showed them where Japan was on the globe, and she propped up a big map of Japan against the board. The class spent the rest of the day making lists of questions to ask Mr. Uchida.

He arrived on Monday. He had gray hair and a very soft voice. He showed them slides of his town and of the children at the school where he taught.

Every day the class learned something new about Japan. Sometimes they pushed all the desks away and sat on straw mats. They practiced eating with chopsticks, and they learned Japanese words.

Emily was disappointed by some of the things that Mr. Uchida told them. Japanese cities looked a lot like American cities—big, modern, and crowded. People wore the same kinds of clothes as they did in America—suits and dresses and even blue jeans.

"But there are some things that are very different," Mr. Uchida told them. He showed them colorful kimonos and wooden clogs. He showed them how to draw with black sumi ink and brushes, and how to write short poems called haiku. You had to count the syllables, five in the first line, then seven, then five in the last line. Each poem was like a puzzle; you had to search for the right-size words.

Emily wrote a haiku about Johnny:

*Is he really mad*
*because I know the answers*
*or is he jealous?*

She wrote haiku about Leo and Ivy:

*He's a funny clown*
*who wears a smile and a joke.*
*My friend cheers me up.*

*She's a bouncing ball.*
*She likes to talk, laugh, and play.*
*She sticks up for me.*

Emily had so much fun writing haiku that she didn't worry about Johnny for a while. But when Mr. Uchida put her haiku up on the board with her sumi ink pictures, she saw Johnny glare at her again.

After Mr. Uchida had been with the class for two weeks, he arrived one afternoon with a basket full of colored paper.

"Today we will begin to learn origami, the art of paper folding."

One by one, he held up tiny figures of birds and animals made out of paper. There was a penguin, a frog, and a crane that even flapped its wings.

Everyone got several sheets of paper. Emily picked green, blue, yellow, and a deep rose.

Ivy picked pink and purple, black and brown.
"I want to make a bear," she said.

Mr. Uchida showed them how to make the first basic folds. Then he gave out instruction sheets for three easy figures—a house, a boat, and a cup.

The first person to finish all three was Johnny Ringer. Mr. Uchida looked carefully at his figures.

"Very well done," he said, and pinned them up on the board. "You may take a more difficult sheet now. You will use the same basic folds, but the figure is more complicated. Follow the directions carefully."

Johnny picked out the penguin sheet. He made the figure out of black paper. Mr. Uchida showed him how to turn the corners into flippers, and how to shape the head and the bill. Johnny's penguin came out perfectly on the very first try.

"You are very good at this, my friend," Mr. Uchida told Johnny. "Let me see your hands."

Johnny held out his hands. He wasn't sure what Mr. Uchida was looking for. Both hands were grimy, with dirt under the nails. There were spots of ink and red marker, but Mr. Uchida didn't seem to notice.

"Look how long and nicely shaped your fingers are. You have very smart fingers, Johnny."

Johnny looked down at his hands, admiring them.

Mr. Uchida patted him on the shoulder. "Take care of those hands. They are a sign of special talent."

Johnny blushed. For once he had nothing to say.

He just smiled quietly and picked another sheet.

From then on, Johnny was the expert at origami. His figures were always the best. His folds were straight. He was careful and sure. He moved quickly but never hurried. Soon he became Mr. Uchida's helper, showing the others how to turn a fold inside out, or how to line up the edges perfectly. The board was covered with Johnny's paper animals.

Emily was just no good at origami. She couldn't get the folds right. She couldn't line up the corners, and she couldn't understand the instructions. Her little figures were wrinkled and dirty from the sweat of her fingers. The harder she tried, the worse her figures became. But she wouldn't give up. She wanted to learn how to make the crane, the graceful little figure that could flap its wings.

She tried and tried. Once, when she looked up, Johnny was watching her. He wasn't laughing. He looked as if he knew just how she felt. Emily quickly looked down at her work again. She felt stupid and clumsy. On purpose, she crumpled a sheet of origami paper into a ball and threw it on the floor. The next time she picked a fresh sheet of paper, Johnny came over to her desk.

He showed her how to line up the corners before making the folds.

"Go slow. Don't rush," he said.

His fingers moved smoothly. Emily followed him, step by step.

"Now I get it!" she said.

Johnny left her on her own, and she finished making the frog and started on the penguin.

That afternoon when she caught Johnny's eye on the playground, he smiled at her instead of glaring or making a face. She waved back.

Soon it was the last week of Mr. Uchida's visit. Emily tried to work up to doing the crane. She got stuck on the bear for a day.

"I'll never get it done," she complained to Ivy.

"So? You can keep on trying after he leaves."

"No. We'll go on to something new. I know it. It's now or never."

She kept on trying.

On Thursday Mr. Uchida wasn't at school.

"This gives us a chance to get ready for Mr. Uchida's good-by party tomorrow. We have all day to prepare our surprise," said Mrs. Higgenbottom. "What should we make for him?"

"Let's make good-by cards with sumi ink," said Ivy.

"And write haiku," said Emily.

"Let's make him a paper kimono to wear at the party," said Mary Louise. "We can paint it with birds and flowers to make it look like silk."

Emily looked across the room. Everyone was talking and making plans. Everyone except Johnny. He sat by himself in the reading corner staring out the window.

Poor Johnny, Emily thought. He's going to miss Mr. Uchida. She sat for a while chewing on her pencil and thinking. Then she raised her hand.

Mrs. Higgenbottom nodded. "What is it, Emily?"

"I think we should decorate the room with origami. All different colors. We can hang them on strings, lots of them, by the windows and in front of the boards and from the lights, too."

"Hey, that'll look great," Ivy said.

Mrs. Higgenbottom agreed. "Good idea. But who will make them all? We haven't much time."

"Johnny!" shouted the class.

Johnny looked up, surprised.

"How about it, Ringer?" called Leo.

"OK," said Johnny. "I guess I can do it."

They spent the day preparing for the party. Emily wrote haiku. Ivy drew pictures. Leo and Phyllis practiced a puppet show. Mary Louise and Patricia worked on the kimono. And Johnny sat by the window and made origami figures.

The class stopped their projects after lunch to learn a Japanese song, and they each wrote a letter to a child in Mr. Uchida's class in Japan.

"I hope they write back," said Leo.

Johnny wrote an extra letter. It was to Mr. Uchida. Emily noticed it when she put her letter in the box.

"Want some help hanging up your animals?" Emily asked Johnny.

He nodded. "But be careful not to bend them."

They strung the figures across the boards and hung them in front of the windows. The wind turned them gently on their threads.

"They look like they're flying," Emily said.

They finished just before the bell rang for the end of school. The room was cleared, with desks pushed against the back wall. The floor was covered with mats, and a few pillows from the reading corner were set out.

"Tomorrow everyone should bring in a pillow to sit on. And remember to take off your shoes outside the room," Mrs. Higgenbottom reminded them. "And, Johnny, be sure to be here a little early. You'll be the class host for the day because you've been Mr. Uchida's special helper."

Johnny stood up very straight and nodded.

The party on Friday was great. Mr. Uchida smiled and clapped at everything. He laughed at the play, admired the paintings, and read every poem out loud.

"My class will enjoy getting your letters, and they will write to you in return, I promise."

When it was time to leave, Mr. Uchida put his arm around Johnny.

"Good-by, special helper. You've been a big help. Don't forget to take care of those hands, and write to me sometime."

Johnny nodded, but he couldn't smile.

Mr. Uchida seemed to understand. He gave him a pat on the head.

Mr. Uchida left after lunch, and the class put the room back in order. Emily watched Johnny carefully take down his little origami figures. He still looked sad.

"I wonder what he's going to do with all those," she thought. She wanted to ask him, but she was a little bit afraid. She remembered how he used to tease her.

But that had been before Mr. Uchida came.

Trying to feel brave, Emily went over to the board where Johnny was working.

"Johnny?"

He looked up.

"What are you going to do with your little animals?"

He shrugged.

"I was wondering . . ." She paused, then started again. "I was hoping that maybe you'd give me one of your cranes. I never did make one, and I really wanted to. I could use yours for a model."

A big smile spread across Johnny's face.

"Sure. I'll pick you out the best."

As the bell rang that afternoon, Johnny gave Emily a perfect crane made out of deep blue paper. He left quickly. She only had time to say, "Thanks," as he ran out the door.

She looked carefully at the little figure. Each fold was perfect. She could imagine it flying over the water. She was about to tuck it between the pages of her library book for safe-keeping on the trip home when she noticed some writing on the underside of the wings.

She turned it over and read the tiny printing: "For Emily from your friend, Johnny."

She put it carefully in her library book. Then she took one of her haiku and sumi ink paintings from her desk, and on the back she wrote, "For Johnny from your friend, Emily." She put it carefully inside Johnny's desk.

Then she whistled happily all the way home.

**Think and Discuss**

1. Why does Johnny Ringer think Emily is a showoff?
2. At first, what does Emily do about it?
3. How do things change after Mr. Uchida arrives?
4. How might Emily have solved her problem with Johnny if Mr. Uchida had not come to school?
5. What do you think Johnny writes to Mr. Uchida in the letter he puts in the box?

● Comprehension Skill: Time sequence

# Communication Workshop

**Talk**

Emily and Johnny both discover that a person may be good at some things and not good at others. Think about the things you do well. What do you find hard to do? Get together with your classmates and discuss what you would like to do better.

Speaking/Listening: Cooperative learning

**Write**

Write a paragraph about something you would like to learn to do better. Say why you want to do this one thing well. Display your paragraph on a class bulletin board. Then share talents with your classmates. Help someone learn to do something that may come easily to you.

Writing Fluency: Paragraph

# Taking a Message

*Liz...*
*A man called to talk to you. He said it*
*was important. He wants you to call him*
*I forgot his number.*
                                    *Sara*

Liz has been waiting to hear if she made the soccer team. If you were Liz, how would you feel about finding a message like Sara's? Liz is angry and wants to know if her sister will ever grow up enough to take a real message. Liz wrote this message to show her sister what to do next time:

*Liz,*
*  Mr. Fox called at 4 P.M. about soccer.*
*You must call him by 6 P.M. His phone*
*number is 237-4040.*
                                    *Sara*

Compare Liz's message to the one Sara left. Which one do you think is better and why?

Part of growing up is learning to take clear and helpful messages. Don't forget these things:

- Say who called and write clearly.
- Get a phone number, or say when the person will call back.
- Don't be afraid to ask someone to repeat the message so you can write it correctly.

# Okay Everybody, Listen to This

by Karla Kuskin

Okay everybody, listen to this:
I am tired of being smaller
Than you
And them
And him
And trees and buildings.
So watch out
All you gorillas and adults
Beginning tomorrow morning
Boy
Am I going to be taller.

# Good-Bye, Six—Hello, Seven

by Judith Viorst

I'm getting a higher bunk bed.
And I'm getting a bigger bike.
And I'm getting to cross Connecticut Avenue
    all by myself, if I like.
And I'm getting to help do dishes.
And I'm getting to weed the yard.
And I'm getting to think that seven
    could be hard.

*Eliza wishes that her family could stay just the way it was before her parents were divorced. As you read about Eliza, find out how Eliza's life has changed and what happens to help Eliza accept those changes.*

# Eliza's Daddy

by Ianthe Thomas

Eliza's daddy was a big, strong man who didn't live with Eliza in her house.

He lived down the block, around the corner, past Colucci's meat market, way on the other side of town. And he had a new family.

He didn't come to Eliza's house very often, but when he did, he would sit on the porch and say, "Tell your mother we'll be back at five o'clock," or "Tell your mother that you'll need a sweater."

He would never tell Eliza's mother anything, anytime, anywhere.

And he never called her "Honey" anymore.

This made Eliza very sad.

She knew that her daddy and mommy were divorced, though, and no matter how much she wanted them to live together again, this just wasn't going to happen.

Now her daddy had a new family, a new wife, a new daughter, and a new baby, who called her father "Daddy."

Eliza's daddy lived with his new family all week, but every Saturday afternoon he would come to Eliza's house to take her out.

"Where do you want to go today, Eliza?" he would ask.

And Eliza would think very hard of a special place to go with her daddy.

Last week on their special day they went to the zoo, and Eliza's daddy had let her eat too much cotton candy.

He never said, "You've had enough junk, Baby," the way he used to. Instead, he let her eat five cotton candy cones until she was sticky and sick all the way home.

Eliza had been dizzy.

Her mother had been angry.

And her father had said, "I'm sorry, Eliza. I shouldn't have let you eat so much."

Then he went over to the other side of town where his new family lived.

That night, Eliza had a dream.

She dreamed she met her father's new daughter.

Her father's new daughter's name was Wonderful Angel Daughter.

Everyone in the world called her Wonderful Angel Daughter. Oh, she was beautiful! Oh, she was smart!

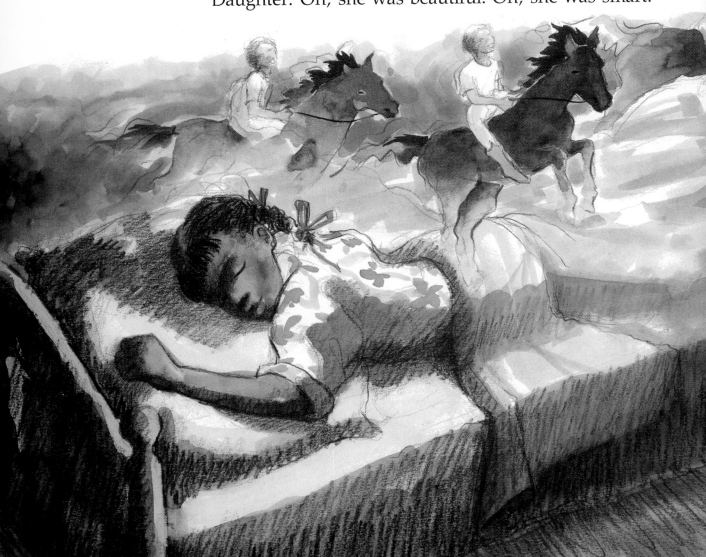

She had been to a ranch in Arizona, and she knew how to ride horses.

She came riding up to Eliza on a beautiful black horse—the most magnificent horse in the world. His name was Wonderful Horse.

"Can you ride a horse, Eliza?" asked Wonderful Angel Daughter.

"Yes," said Eliza softly, even though she knew she couldn't.

"Well, then, here's your horse." Beautiful Wonderful Angel Daughter laughed.

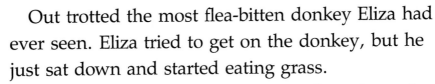

Out trotted the most flea-bitten donkey Eliza had ever seen. Eliza tried to get on the donkey, but he just sat down and started eating grass.

Eliza was begging him to get up when she woke up. "Oh, what a horrible dream," she thought as she picked herself up from the floor. She tried to go back to sleep, but she couldn't. All she could think about was her father's new daughter.

"Just suppose she does have a horse," thought Eliza. "Just suppose she has the most beautiful black horse in the world. Just suppose she's been to a ranch in Arizona. Maybe she has done everything in the world," thought Eliza sadly.

Every day she thought more and more about her daddy's new daughter. Eliza wondered what kind of clothes she wore. She wondered if she could speak Spanish. She wondered if she had a bicycle. She wondered if she could stand on her head without someone's holding her feet. She wondered so much about her daddy's new daughter that she decided to ask him if she could come to his house.

On Friday night, Eliza set her clothes out for Saturday. She was going to wear her striped overalls and her pointed-toe cowboy boots.

Just before she got into bed, she stood in front of the mirror practicing what she was going to say to her daddy.

She decided to say, "Daddy, may I come to your house?" Eliza thought that this was the most polite way to ask.

But on Saturday, when her father said, "What do you want to do today, Eliza?" she said, "I want to . . . I want to . . . uh, I want to . . . to go to the park."

"OK," said Daddy.

And they went to the park.

That night when she was putting on her pajamas, she said to herself, "Next Saturday I'm really going to ask him."

So she practiced saying, "Daddy, may I come to your house?" every single night until she was sure she could do it right.

On Saturday, before her father even had a chance to ask her what she wanted to do, Eliza said, "Daddy, may I come to your house?"—just the way she had practiced all week.

"Do you really want to go there, Eliza?" her father asked.

"Yes, Daddy," she said. "More than anything else."

"OK, Eliza," Daddy said.

They got in his car and drove all the way across town—past Mrs. Wilkes, sitting under her wisteria bush, past a kitten crying in front of Colucci's market—all the way over to the other side of town.

All the way across town to a big house, where there was a girl about Eliza's age playing in the yard and a baby, sitting in a yellow stroller, who called Eliza's father "Daddy."

I. M. C.

"Hi," said the girl, running up to Eliza. "I'm Mandy."

"Hi. I'm Eliza."

"Can you ride a horse, Mandy?" asked Eliza.

"No. I never have," said Mandy sadly.

"Neither can I," said Eliza.

"Why don't we ask Daddy to take us riding today?" said Mandy, smiling.

"That would be great," said Eliza.

They ran to Eliza and Mandy's daddy and asked him.

So he took them riding—together.

## Meet the Author

Ianthe Thomas liked to make up stories when she was a little girl. She would tell her pretend stories over and over again: "Make-a-pretend-that my Daddy is coming to the train station. He has a big suitcase . . ."

Ianthe's father, like Eliza's daddy, did not live with her and her mother. The special story Ianthe Thomas told herself about his visits helped her feel close to him. When Ianthe grew up, she told this story another way and it became the book *Eliza's Daddy*. "I was thinking about my father," she explains. "I was remembering all the good times I had with him, all the times he listened to me and laughed with me."

Ianthe Thomas's story helped her hold on to those good times, but it also helped her grow. She remembers her father saying to her: "Take your time. Just be quiet a moment. Think. Say what you want to say. Make it simple. Speak with your heart. Say how you are really feeling. This will make everything better."

"My father was right . . . I was happy to know he loved me, even though he didn't see me every day." Ianthe Thomas, like Eliza, learned that "although nothing is perfect, it is still good."

# Comprehension Check

**Think and Discuss**

1. What changes have happened in Eliza's family?
- 2. What happens to help Eliza accept those changes?
3. What do you think Eliza's dream says about her feelings?
- 4. Why does Eliza have such a hard time asking her father if she may visit his new family?
5. Do you think Eliza does the right thing by going to meet Mandy?

- Comprehension Skill: Cause and effect

# Communication Workshop

**Talk**

Going through changes in a family can be one of the hard parts of growing up. If you were Eliza's friend, what kinds of things might you do or say to help her feel better? Choose a partner and role-play the parts of Eliza and Eliza's friend.

Speaking/Listening: Role-playing

**Write**

Write a letter that Eliza might send into an advice column in the newspaper. Tell about changes in Eliza's family. Exchange letters with your partner. Pretend you are the advice columnist and answer your partner's letter.

Writing Fluency: Letter

# LOOKING BACK

**Thinking and Writing About the Section**

| | |
|---|---|
| Prewriting | Each character in this section grows up a little by learning something. Picture each character in a certain scene. You can write a descriptive paragraph about what you picture to share with a partner. First copy this chart and fill it in. |

*See your Thinker's Handbook for tips.*

| Character | One Scene | Words to Describe the Character |
|---|---|---|
| Michael | | |
| Johnny | | angry eyes, clenched fist |
| Eliza | meeting her half sister | |

**Writing**

Choose one of the characters and write a paragraph to describe the character in the scene you listed. Use specific words to describe the character's looks or actions. For more help with descriptive paragraphs, see your Writer's Handbook.

**Revising**

Read your first draft to a partner. Have you used details so your partner can "see" the character? Make changes, proofread, and write your final copy.

**Presenting**

Read your paragraph to your partner. Ask him or her to draw what you have described!

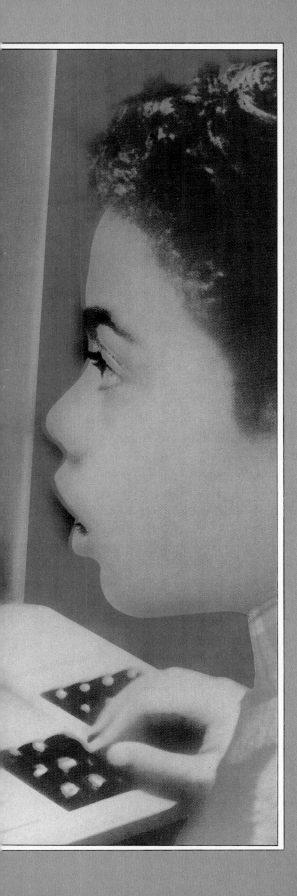

# 6

# Figuring It Out

WHAT'S HAPPENING HERE? Are you good at solving problems and figuring things out?

Next you will read about a make-believe character who solved a problem for a pickle company, a real person who knew what to do in an emergency, and a bear with a most unusual problem, whose friends help him figure it out.

# Finding Details

Have you ever needed to find your way back to a place you liked or a store you wanted to go to again? To help yourself remember a place, you probably thought back to things you saw, smelled, or heard on the way to that place the first time.

Each thing you remembered was a **detail,** or a small piece of information, that helped you find that special place. A sign, a building, or a certain sound or smell are all details that might help you remember where you were.

When you read, you come across many kinds of details. Look for important details in what you read, because these details often lead up to a big point. Sometimes, details help you figure out an author's reason for writing something, or help you to understand the points he or she is making. Some details tell you more about what is happening in a story, or give you important information about the characters and setting. Details often help you picture what you read.

*Now what was the name of that bakery?*

Use the details in the next paragraph to understand how Carmen goes about her day. See how she uses details to figure things out.

Carmen's schoolbus was sometimes late in the winter, but never this late. For a moment Carmen wondered if she was at the wrong corner. She tapped the sidewalk around her with her cane, but there was no one around. She listened closely. A heavy, groaning sound came from far down the street. Finally, the sound stopped in front of her. SLIDE, FLAP! were the next sounds, and warm air touched her face. "It *is* the right corner after all," thought Carmen.

1. Which detail first tells you that Carmen's bus is coming?

Did you say that the *heavy, groaning sound* is the first detail that tells you a bus is near? Often, sounds are details that help us picture what is happening in a story.

2. What two details tell you that the doors of the bus have opened?

You know that the doors have opened when Carmen hears the SLIDE, FLAP! of the doors and she feels warm air on her face.

**3.** What things did you learn about Carmen?

**4.** Which details help you know these things?

## Practicing Finding Details

Read the next paragraph about black bears. Look for details that help you picture these animals. Notice how other details lead up to the point the author is making about them.

Two black bears were walking along Creek Road—a mother bear and her fat, little cub. The cub ran up to his mother every now and then, trying to make her play. These animals were wonderful to watch—from far away. A mother bear will use her long, sharp claws and teeth to fight if she thinks her cub is in danger. When scared or angry, bears have been known to kill people.

**1.** How do you feel about the bears at the beginning? Which details make you feel this way?

**2.** What point is the author making about bears? Which details make you think this?

## Tips for Reading on Your Own

- Find details that tell you more about a story, the characters, or its setting.
- Look for important details that help you understand the points an author is making.

*The Pleasant Pickle Company has a big problem, and only Chameleon can help figure it out. Read to find out how Chameleon does it. As you read, look for the important detail that makes Chameleon perfect for the job he's hired to do.*

# Chameleon Was a Spy

by Diane Redfield Massie

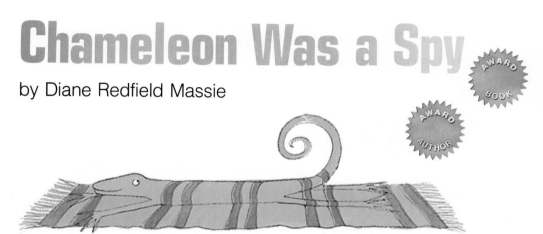

Chameleon liked to change colors. He could match the rug and the chair.

He could match the walls and the curtains. "I can match anything," said Chameleon. "You name it."

It was hard for his mother to find him, even upside down in the parlor. "CHAMELEON!" she would call next to him. "WHERE ARE YOU?"

Chameleon practiced every day, changing his colors from red to green, or from pink to purple and blue. He could manage every color in the rainbow, adding dots and stripes and even zigzags as needed.

"I shall be a spy when I grow up," said Chameleon. "No one will ever catch me."

One day Chameleon noticed a small advertisement in the newspaper. "WANTED," it said, "RELIABLE PERSON FOR SUPER SECRET WORK. Come to: 222 South Bean Street."

"How exciting!" said Chameleon, leaning against the refrigerator. He turned as snowy white as the door just for practice.

"Chameleon," said his mother. "Where *are* you?"

"I'm going to get a job," said Chameleon, becoming as yellow as the wall. "Wish me luck."

"Good luck," said his mother. "Is that you by the door?"

Chameleon waved good-bye and ran down the road to town, turning green and brown to match the countryside.

At last he came to the Pleasant Pickle Company. Chameleon knocked loudly. The door opened.

"Who's there?" said a voice.

"It's Chameleon," said Chameleon, turning as brown as the door.

"Where?" asked the voice. "I don't see anyone!" A man with a bushy beard looked out. He looked up and down the street.

"I'm right here," said Chameleon, waving his arms.

"GOOD HEAVENS!" said the man, "A FROG!"

"I'm *not* a frog," said Chameleon. "I'm a chameleon."

"What do you want?" asked the man.

"A job," said Chameleon. "What's the super secret work?"

"I can't tell you," said the man. "Follow me."

Chameleon followed him down a long hall, which led to an office. They went inside. Nine men and a potted plant sat around a long table.

"May I present Mr. Chameleon," the man said.

"Where *is* he?" asked the president of the company.

"He's right here, somewhere," said the man with the bushy beard, looking about.

"Here I am," said Chameleon. He leaped onto the table.

"A FROG?" said everyone.

"I am a chameleon!" said Chameleon loudly. "And I am here about the super secret job. What kind of work *is* it?" he asked.

"Spying," said the president.

"WOW!" said Chameleon.

"Pleasant Pickles have always been the best!" the president said, pounding his fist on the table. "But *now* . . . THE PERFECT PICKLE COMPANY HAS *OUR* SECRET FORMULA!" he shouted. "THEY'VE STOLEN IT!"

"How?" asked Chameleon.

"A pickle scientist took it," said the man with the bushy beard. "He works for the Perfect Pickle Company."

"WE MUST NOT BE SECOND BEST!" cried the president. "WE MUST GET OUR FORMULA BACK!"

"I'll get it!" said Chameleon. Then, to show what he could do, he jumped to the plant. He turned as green as a leaf.

"Where is he?" asked everyone.

"Here I am," said Chameleon. He jumped off onto the coffeepot. His skin was a coppery orange. "Guess where I am *now*," he said.

Everyone hunted about the room, looking under their chairs.

"Where is he? I don't see him. Can you find him? I can't," they said.

"Well," said Chameleon. He leaped back to the table again. "What do you say?"

"YOU'RE HIRED!" cried the president.

"A perfect spy," said everyone. "Chameleon will get that formula!"

The next day, Chameleon went to the Perfect Pickle Company plant. He went inside, sliding along the pale tan walls, matching them perfectly.

LABORATORIES said a sign on a door. Chameleon opened it. He saw tables and bottles and jars. There were tubs of pickles sitting everywhere.

"This must be where they make the formula," he said. He waited next to a tub.

Soon a scientist in a long white coat came in. His beard was pale orange. It hung down to his buttons. "Now that *I* have the Pleasant Pickle formula," he said, "Pleasant Pickles will soon go out of business! Hee, hee, hee!" He sprinkled a bit of salt in the pickle tub next to Chameleon.

"THE PERFECT PICKLE COMPANY WILL MAKE MILLIONS!" he shouted, "MILLIONS!"

"Good heavens!" said his assistant, coming in the door. "Is anything wrong?"

"WRONG?" cried the scientist. "HOW CAN ANYTHING BE WRONG, YOU BOTTLE-BRAIN! WE HAVE THE FORMULA!"

"Where is it?" asked his assistant.

"Here!" said the scientist, flinging it down on the table. "No one else shall ever see it!"

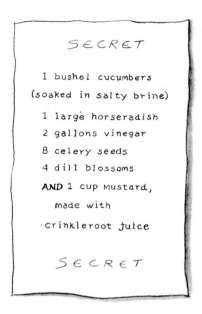

SECRET

1 bushel cucumbers
(soaked in salty brine)
1 large horseradish
2 gallons vinegar
8 celery seeds
4 dill blossoms
AND 1 cup mustard,
made with
crinkleroot juice

SECRET

Chameleon slid around the pickle tub. He could see the formula. It was next to the scientist's hand. He turned his skin white as the table, and crept slowly out.

The scientist reached for the formula. Chameleon slipped under the paper and clung to the top.

"What's this?" said the scientist, turning the paper over.

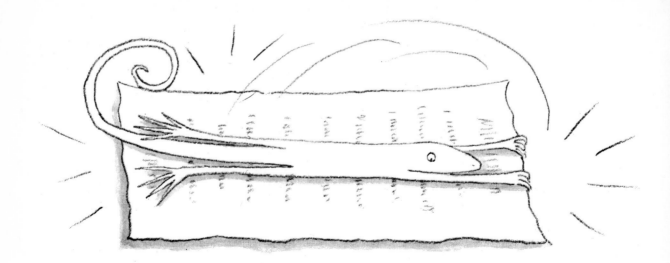

Chameleon flipped over to the front side, and the formula fell to the table, CLUNK!

Chameleon slid to the bottom and lay still. His skin matched the words beneath him perfectly.

"Crinkleroot juice," they said.

"WAIT!" snapped the scientist, staring at the page. "Eyes are looking out of the formula!"

"Eyes?" said his assistant.

"Quiet! I must get to the bottom of this!" His hand closed over Chameleon.

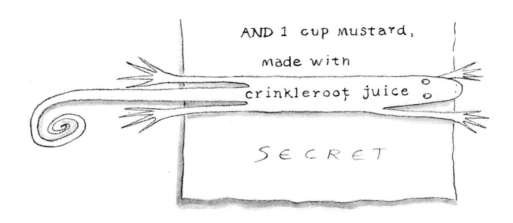

Chameleon turned green as a pickle.

"AHA!" cried the scientist, holding Chameleon by the tail. "What have we *here?*"

"It's a pickle," said the assistant.

"It's a frog," said the scientist.

"I'm a chameleon," said Chameleon.

"WHAT," roared the scientist, "are you doing here?"

"Just looking around," said Chameleon. He stared at the formula beneath him as he swung back and forth.

"You were reading the secret formula!" said the scientist. "YOU ARE A SPY!"

Chameleon twisted loose and leaped to the table. He grabbed the secret formula and jumped down to the floor.

"AFTER HIM!" cried the scientist. "HE MUST NOT GET AWAY!"

Chameleon ran down the hall. The door at the end
said PICKLING PLANT. He hurried inside.

There were tubs of pickles everywhere. Chameleon
ran up a ramp. He could see a long row of bottles
moving along below him. The bottles were passing
under a chute which filled them up with pickles.

"STOP HIM!" shouted the scientist, rushing through
the door.

Chameleon leaped to the pickle chute. But his foot
slipped. Down, down, down, he fell. PLUNK! into a
bottle. Pickles poured down from the pickle chute.

"HELP!" yelled Chameleon. Pickles surrounded him, and one lay on his head. The formula sank to the bottom.

"HELP! HELP!"

CLAMP! went the lid on the bottle. SWUP! went the label in front.

"HELP! HELP!" yelled Chameleon inside the bottle, but no one heard him. His bottle moved along with all the other bottles. He pushed up the lid just a crack.

"Number 936,073,492," said the checker at the end of the line.

Chameleon waved his arms. But his bottle moved into a box with eleven other bottles, all filled with pickles.

The box lid came down, FLUMP! It was very dark.

"I'm not a pickle," said Chameleon to himself. "I'm a chameleon." He settled himself on top of a pickle and dozed in the darkness.

After a very long time, Chameleon felt himself tipping back and forth. The pickles bumped against him, and the pickle juice sloshed against his chin. "We're moving somewhere," he said.

THUMP! Creeeeet, creeeet, pop! The box lid came off, letting bright daylight in. Chameleon covered his eyes. It was much too bright to see.

Slosh! Slosh! went the pickle juice. The pickles bumped his sides.

CLUNK! CLUNK! Then everything was still.

Chameleon uncovered his eyes. He saw rows and rows of cans and jars, sitting on long shelves. "Where am I?" he said.

An old man passed him, pushing a basket. He stopped in front of the pickles.

"I'm in a market!" Chameleon cried. He waved his arms and pounded on the glass. But the old man didn't see or hear him. He pushed his basket slowly away.

Chameleon pushed hard on the lid above him, but he could not make the crack wider. "This is awful!" he said. "I could wait on this shelf for months before someone buys me!" He bit off a piece of pickle and chewed it slowly, thinking.

"I'll turn bright red," he said.

"*Then* someone's sure to notice me." He turned his skin crimson and moved about, waving his arms and legs.

"Mommy," said a little girl. "Look at that funny pickle."

"What pickle?" said her mother, reading her market list. She picked up Chameleon's jar and dropped it into her basket.

"Saved at last!" said Chameleon.

"Let me see the pickle," said the little girl.

"Don't bother me," said her mother, reading her list. A large bag of noodles dropped into the basket. It lay over Chameleon's jar. "Pickles and noodles," said the mother. They moved quickly to the front of the store.

"Next," said the manager.

Chameleon's jar sat on the counter. The clerk picked it up. Chameleon waved and smiled.

"WHAT'S *THAT?*" cried the little girl's mother.

"I'LL CALL THE FOOD INSPECTOR!" shouted the manager.

The food inspector came in a rush.

"A CONTAMINATED BOTTLE OF PICKLES!" he said. "THE PICKLES IN THIS BOTTLE ARE NOT FIT TO EAT!"

"Let me out!" shouted Chameleon. But no one heard him.

The photographers came from the paper. They photographed Chameleon's jar. Someone put the jar in a bag and carried it off to the police station.

"PERFECT PICKLE CO. CLOSED!" said the papers the next day. "A CONTAMINATED JAR OF PICKLES IS FOUND ON A MARKET SHELF!"

When Chameleon's mother saw the paper that morning, she hurried down to town.

"LET MY SON OUT OF THAT JAR!" she said.

312

The police chief took off the lid.

"Thank you," said Chameleon, dripping pickle juice over the desk. He followed his mother out the door and hurried home.

"Chameleon," said his mother at breakfast, "how did you like your new job?"

"It was all right," said Chameleon, "if you like being a pickle."

The telephone rang.

"Hello," answered Chameleon.

"I've read the morning paper," said the president of the Pleasant Pickle Company. "Good work!"

"Thank you," said Chameleon.

"Did you get the formula . . . ?"

"Yes," said Chameleon.

"YAHOOOOOOOOOO!" yelled the president into the telephone.

"I'll be right down," said Chameleon.

He hurried down to 222 South Bean Street. Before he could knock, the door opened.

"THERE HE IS!" shouted everyone. They carried Chameleon inside. Balloons hung from the céiling.

"Where is the formula?" asked the president.

Chameleon held up the wrinkled paper. "Here it is!" he said proudly. Everyone clapped.

"I'll copy it on the blackboard," said the president. "Let me have it."

He started to read out loud and stopped.

"The writing at the bottom is blurred," he shouted. "The last ingredient is missing!"

"MISSING?" cried everyone.

"Our secret formula is *worthless* without it!" groaned the president. "What *shall* we do?"

"Ohhhhhhhhhhhhhhhhhhh!" said everyone.

A balloon popped.

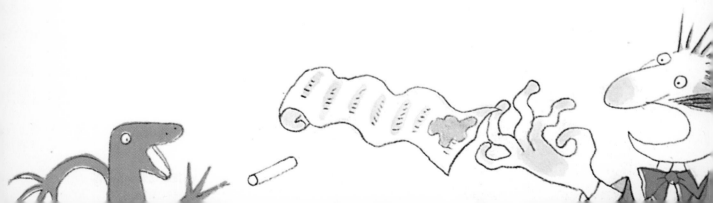

"WAIT!" cried Chameleon.

He grabbed the secret formula, and lay across the bottom where the last line had been.

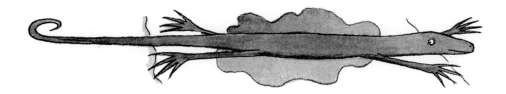

Spots and swirls flickered over his back.

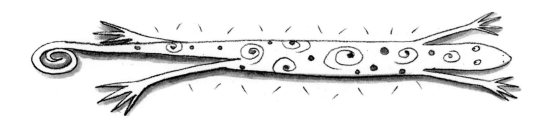

Dots and dashes flashed on and off, and then . . .

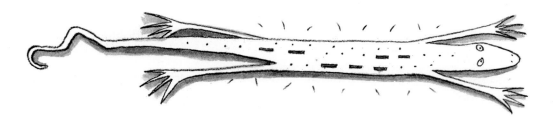

All at once . . . two words appeared, in large clear letters: "Crinkleroot juice."

"THAT'S IT!" shouted the president. "Chameleon has saved our formula!"

"HOORAY for Chameleon!" yelled everyone.

The president wrote "crinkleroot juice" on the blackboard while everyone cheered. Then he presented Chameleon with a gold plaque. It said:

For CHAMELEON, THE PERFECT SPY . . . with thanks from THE PLEASANT PICKLE COMPANY, makers of THE WORLD'S BEST PICKLES.

### Meet the Author/Illustrator

Not even a chameleon could do all that Diane Redfield Massie has done in her life. She started out as a musician but is now a writer of children's books. She also loves doing things for the theater, such as writing and acting in her own plays and making costumes.

Massie is also an artist. She has drawn the art for all her books, including *Chameleon Was a Spy*.

Musician, writer, costume-maker, artist—what will Massie turn to next?

Massie's other books include *The Baby Bee Bee Bird, A Turtle and a Loon, A Birthday for Bird, MacGregor Was a Dog,* and *The Komodo Dragon's Jewels.*

# Comprehension Check

*See your Thinker's Handbook for tips.*

## Think and Discuss

1. What problem does the Pleasant Pickle Company have?
2. How does Chameleon solve the Pleasant Pickle Company's problem?
• 3. What important detail about Chameleon makes him perfect to be a spy?
4. What happens to the formula while Chameleon is in the pickle jar?
• 5. Reread the third paragraph on page 306. Why is this detail important to remember?

• Comprehension Skill: Details

# Communication Workshop

## Talk

Discuss with your classmates other jobs Chameleon could do well. Name as many different jobs as you can, telling why Chameleon would be perfect for them.

Speaking/Listening: Cooperative learning

## Write

Imagine that you have a job for Chameleon. Write a newspaper ad for the job, saying what he would do, how many hours he would work, and what his pay would be. Help your class put all the ads together to make a Classified section of a newspaper.

Writing Fluency: Ad

*As you read this article, think about what is most important to remember in an emergency. Look for new ideas in each paragraph that tell you more information about the topic.*

# What to Do in Emergencies

by Charnan Simon

Lisa Hobel was an average ten-year-old, but one day in 1984 she did something that made her a heroine. Lisa was on her way to school when she stopped to pick up her friend Brittney Behning. As Brittney was leaving, she bumped into the door of her house. Her arm went right through the door, sending glass flying. One piece of glass hit Lisa just above the eye. Lisa wasn't hurt badly, but Brittney's arm was bleeding heavily.

The sight of all that blood was scary, but Lisa knew just what to do. She took Brittney inside the house and called Brittney's mother. Then she made Brittney lie down and covered her with a blanket. She pressed hard on Brittney's arm to stop the bleeding.

When the bleeding stopped, Brittney's mother took the girls to the hospital. Both girls had to have stitches.

If it had not been for Lisa's quick thinking, Brittney might have lost a lot more blood. She might even have died! If you had been Lisa, would you have known what to do?

**Rules for Emergencies**

Here are some important things to remember in an emergency. First, *stay calm.* When you see someone in trouble, it is easy to become frightened. But when you are frightened, you can't think clearly. You make mistakes, and that's the worst thing you can do when you are helping a person who is hurt.

The second rule is *know how to get help.* Lisa called her friend's mother right away. If your parents are away, or if you are not at home or in school when an emergency happens, use the telephone. Learn the emergency numbers you might need. Write them down near your telephone or keep them in your school notebook.

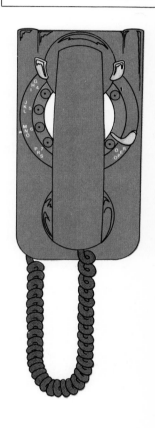

General Emergencies: *911*
Police: *744-5000*
Fire: *744-5000*
Doctor: *910-0528*
Poison Center: *942-5969*
Mom at work: *864-9800*
Dad at work: *852-5270*

If you can't remember any other number, you can always call "0" for operator. If you need to use a pay phone and you don't have money, you can still dial "0" and ask an operator to get help.

Another important rule in an emergency is to *make the hurt person lie still.* Then *cover the person with a coat or blanket.* There are two good reasons for this.

**shock** (shok), state or condition that a badly hurt person goes into. The skin of a person in shock feels very cold.

The first reason is that someone who is hurt often goes into **shock.** This is not the kind of shock you get from electricity. You may look all right, and you may even say you feel all right. But when you are in shock, parts of your body do not work well. You may not be able to breathe easily. If you're badly hurt, you could even die from shock.

There is another reason a hurt person should always lie flat. Inside, the person may be hurt in ways you cannot see. He or she may have broken bones, or may be bleeding inside. Either of these can be very dangerous. You could cause more bleeding and pain if you tried to move the person. After you've made the person keep warm and still, call for help.

## What to Do in Cases of Bleeding

Often, a hurt person is bleeding on the outside, where you can see it. Then you need to stop the bleeding right away. A person can bleed to death in one minute if the cut is big enough.

Call an adult right away. If no one is there, call a doctor by using the operator if you don't have a doctor's number by the phone.

Then it may not be too hard to stop bleeding. All you have to do is *press hard right on the cut,* just as Lisa did. Use a piece of your clothes to do this if there is nothing clean around you, or just use your hand. Put it flat on the cut and press hard. The important thing is to keep pressing until the bleeding stops.

Once the bleeding has stopped a little, call a doctor. Stitches may be needed to keep the cut from opening up and bleeding again.

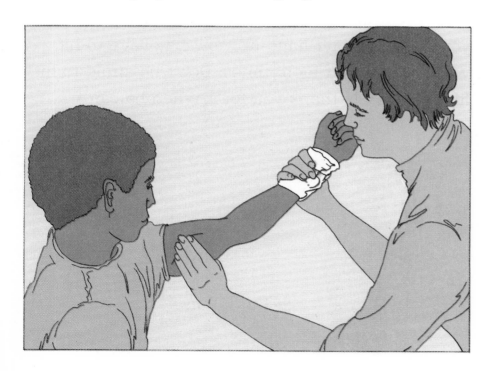

**What to Do in Cases of Choking**

People can choke suddenly, and that is also very scary. One minute your brother is happily eating an apple. The next minute he is coughing and turning red. He looks as if he can't breathe. What should you do?

Again the first rule is to *stay calm.* If your brother can talk, cough, or breathe, he is getting enough air. Tell him to keep coughing until the piece of apple comes up. But if he can't talk, cough, or breathe, act quickly!

First, call an adult. Then stand behind your brother, put one hand on his chest, and help him lean way over, toward the front. Hit him hard, four times, right between the shoulders.

If your brother is still choking, *call the emergency number* by your telephone right away. Tell the person who answers that your brother can't breathe. Be sure to tell that person where you live, but don't hang up. You may have to hit your brother four more times. Don't be afraid to hit him hard. He'll thank you for it when he can breathe again.

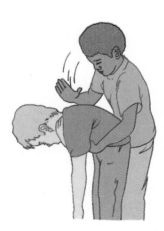

## What to Do in Cases of Poisoning

**Poisons** can make you very sick, maybe even kill you if they get inside your body.

There are lots of poisons around your house. The cleaner in your bathroom is poisonous. So is the paint on your back porch. Too much medicine, or the wrong kind of medicine, can be poisonous. Keep all poisons away from young children. NEVER eat anything that isn't food!

What if you catch your baby sister eating out of the box of laundry soap? There are two things you can do in this emergency. First, have your sister drink a big glass of water or milk. This will make the poison work more slowly in her body. Second, call an adult. If no one is home and you can't reach your parents, call a doctor right away, or call the emergency number for poison on your list. Then keep your sister quiet until help comes. Don't try to make her eat anything else, and don't try to make her throw up! That could make the poison hurt her even more!

**poisons** (poi′zns), things that are dangerous to eat or drink.

## Where to Learn More About Emergencies

Emergencies can happen to anyone, at any time. What Lisa Hobel did shows that we will be better able to help someone in trouble if we take time to learn more about emergencies before they happen. If you would like to learn more safety rules, talk to your parents or teacher and ask what they would want you to do in an emergency. You can also write to the American Red Cross.

**Did You Know?**
The American Red Cross can teach you a lot about safety. It gives classes on safety in schools, libraries, and hospitals all over the United States.

*Think and Discuss*

- 1. What is the topic of this article?
- 2. Which of the following is the main idea?
    a. Knowing what to do in an emergency is very important.
    b. Lisa did a good job of helping Brittney.
- 3. What are three details in the paragraph on page 319 that tell you how Lisa saved Brittney's life?
- 4. What are the two most important rules to remember in an emergency?
- 5. Do you think Lisa is an average ten-year-old?

Comprehension Skill: Main idea and supporting details

## Communication Workshop

*Talk*

Sit in a circle with a group of your classmates. Tell one another about emergencies you've seen or heard about in which calling for help right away is the best thing to do.

Speaking/Listening: Class discussion

*Write*

Make your own list of emergency numbers to carry with you wherever you go. Copy your list for your family and display it near the telephone.

Writing Fluency: List

# Understanding Bike Safety Signs

You've already learned something about safety in your home, so now's the time to learn something about safety on the road.

Just as car drivers have to learn about traffic signs, you have to learn what bike safety signs mean before you get out on the road on a bike.

Some bike signs are shown below. Learn what they mean before you ride your bike on the street.

 Don't ride your bike here.

 You may ride your bike here.

 Drivers, watch out for bike riders!

 This lane is for bikes only.

 Drivers, watch out; bike riders cross the road here.

 This path has been made just for bikes: use it!

 Any cars that are going to turn should let bike riders go first.

*A funny thing happens to Pooh during his visit with Rabbit. This selection will help you see that even the most unusual problems can be figured out, with a little help from friends.*

# Pooh Gets Into a Tight Place

by A. A. Milne

Edward Bear, known to his friends as Winnie-the-Pooh, or Pooh for short, was walking through the forest one day, humming proudly to himself. He had made up a little hum that very morning, as he was doing his Stoutness Exercises in front of the glass: *Tra-la-la, tra-la-la,* as he stretched up as high as he could go, and then *Tra-la-la, tra-la—oh help!—la,* as he tried to reach his toes.

After breakfast he had said it over and over to himself until he had learned it off by heart, and now he was humming it right through, properly. It went like this:

*Tra-la-la, tra-la-la,*
*Tra-la-la, tra-la-la,*
*Rum-tum-tiddle-um-tum.*
*Tiddle-iddle, tiddle-iddle,*
*Tiddle-iddle, tiddle-iddle,*
*Rum-tum-tum-tiddle-um.*

Well, he was humming this hum to himself, and walking along gaily, wondering what everybody else was doing, and what it felt like, being somebody

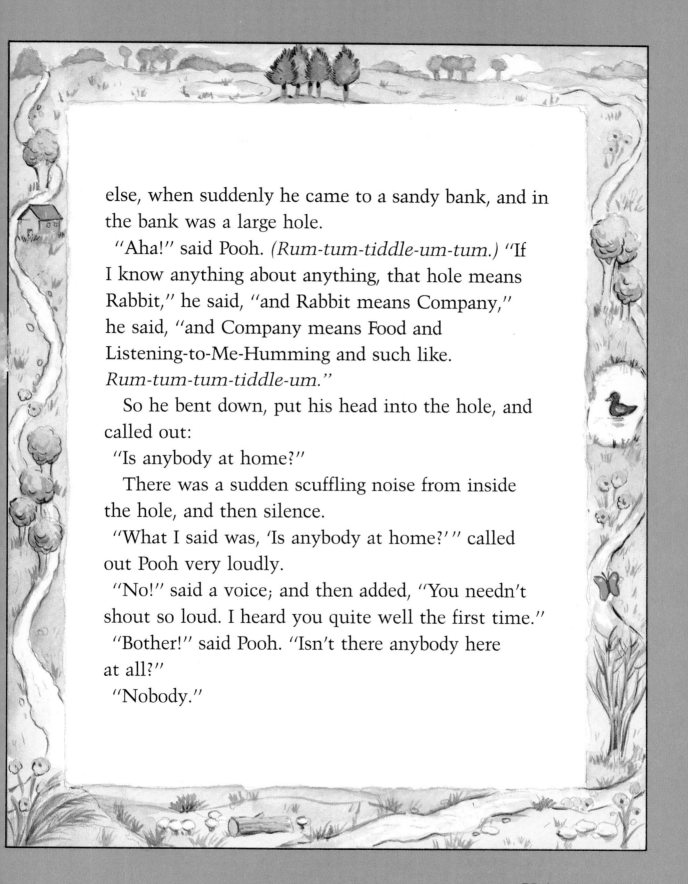

else, when suddenly he came to a sandy bank, and in the bank was a large hole.

"Aha!" said Pooh. *(Rum-tum-tiddle-um-tum.)* "If I know anything about anything, that hole means Rabbit," he said, "and Rabbit means Company," he said, "and Company means Food and Listening-to-Me-Humming and such like. *Rum-tum-tum-tiddle-um.*"

So he bent down, put his head into the hole, and called out:

"Is anybody at home?"

There was a sudden scuffling noise from inside the hole, and then silence.

"What I said was, 'Is anybody at home?'" called out Pooh very loudly.

"No!" said a voice; and then added, "You needn't shout so loud. I heard you quite well the first time."

"Bother!" said Pooh. "Isn't there anybody here at all?"

"Nobody."

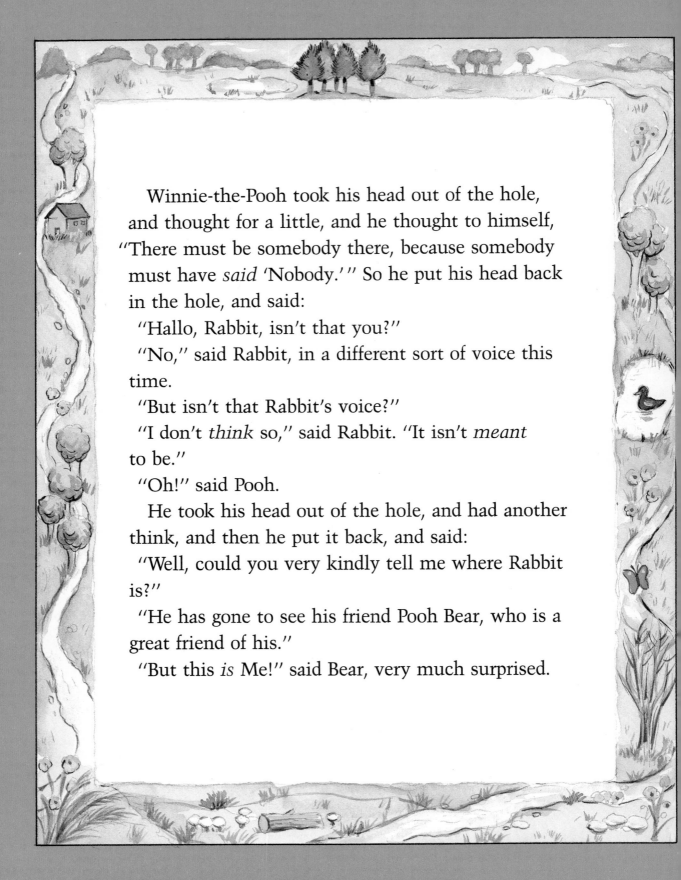

Winnie-the-Pooh took his head out of the hole, and thought for a little, and he thought to himself, "There must be somebody there, because somebody must have *said* 'Nobody.'" So he put his head back in the hole, and said:

"Hallo, Rabbit, isn't that you?"

"No," said Rabbit, in a different sort of voice this time.

"But isn't that Rabbit's voice?"

"I don't *think* so," said Rabbit. "It isn't *meant* to be."

"Oh!" said Pooh.

He took his head out of the hole, and had another think, and then he put it back, and said:

"Well, could you very kindly tell me where Rabbit is?"

"He has gone to see his friend Pooh Bear, who is a great friend of his."

"But this *is* Me!" said Bear, very much surprised.

"What sort of Me?"

"Pooh Bear."

"Are you sure?" said Rabbit, still more surprised.

"Quite, quite sure," said Pooh.

"Oh, well, then, come in."

So Pooh pushed and pushed and pushed his way through the hole, and at last he got in.

"You were quite right," said Rabbit, looking at him all over. "It *is* you. Glad to see you."

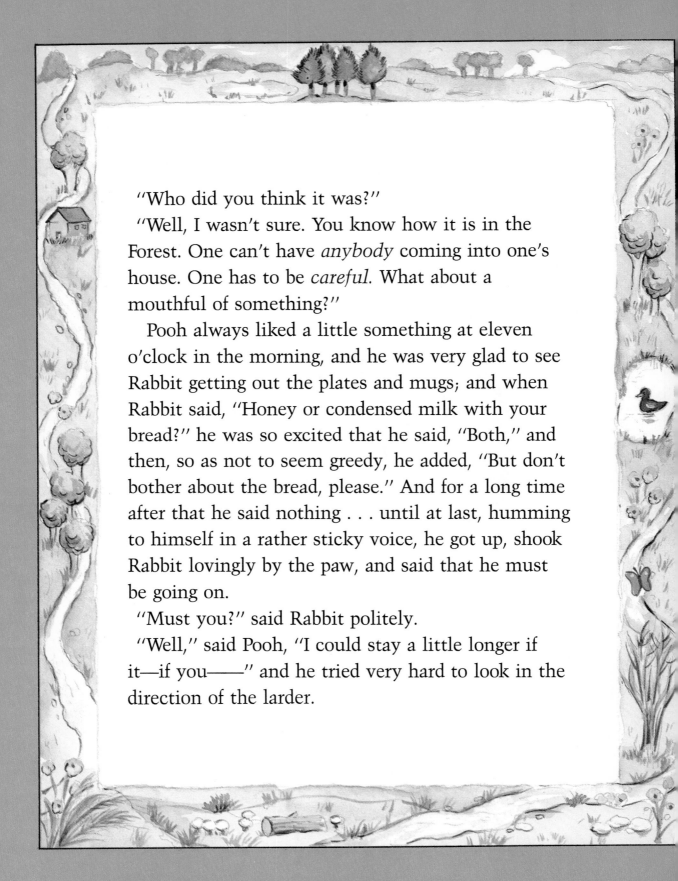

"Who did you think it was?"

"Well, I wasn't sure. You know how it is in the Forest. One can't have *anybody* coming into one's house. One has to be *careful*. What about a mouthful of something?"

Pooh always liked a little something at eleven o'clock in the morning, and he was very glad to see Rabbit getting out the plates and mugs; and when Rabbit said, "Honey or condensed milk with your bread?" he was so excited that he said, "Both," and then, so as not to seem greedy, he added, "But don't bother about the bread, please." And for a long time after that he said nothing . . . until at last, humming to himself in a rather sticky voice, he got up, shook Rabbit lovingly by the paw, and said that he must be going on.

"Must you?" said Rabbit politely.

"Well," said Pooh, "I could stay a little longer if it—if you——" and he tried very hard to look in the direction of the larder.

"As a matter of fact," said Rabbit, "I was going out myself directly."

"Oh, well, then, I'll be going on. Good-by."

"Well, good-by, if you're sure you won't have any more."

"*Is* there any more?" asked Pooh quickly.

Rabbit took the covers off the dishes, and said, "No, there wasn't."

"I thought not," said Pooh, nodding to himself. "Well, good-by. I must be going on."

So he started to climb out of the hole. He pulled with his front paws, and pushed with his back paws, and in a little while his nose was out in the open again . . . and then his ears . . . and then his front paws . . . and then his shoulders . . . and then——

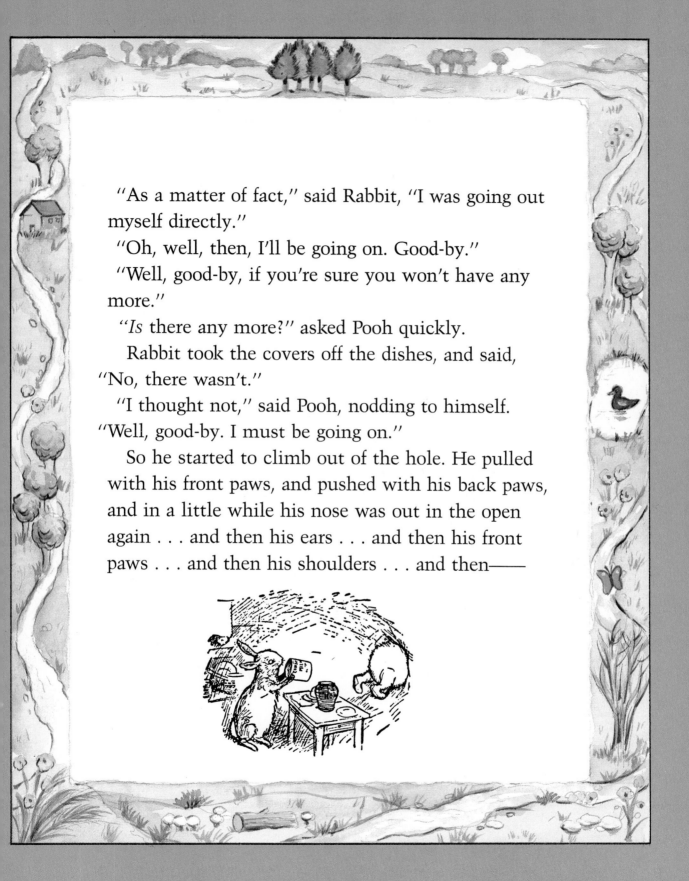

"Oh, help!" said Pooh. "I'd better go back."

"Oh, bother!" said Pooh. "I shall have to go on."

"I can't do either!" said Pooh. "Oh, help *and* bother!"

Now by this time Rabbit wanted to go for a walk too, and finding the front door full, he went out by

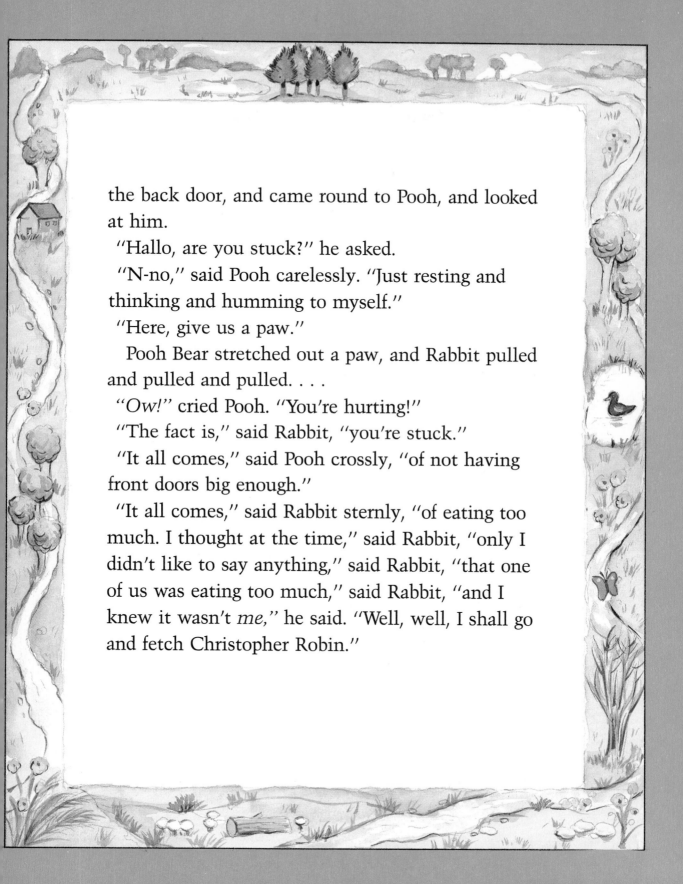

the back door, and came round to Pooh, and looked at him.

"Hallo, are you stuck?" he asked.

"N-no," said Pooh carelessly. "Just resting and thinking and humming to myself."

"Here, give us a paw."

Pooh Bear stretched out a paw, and Rabbit pulled and pulled and pulled. . . .

"*Ow!*" cried Pooh. "You're hurting!"

"The fact is," said Rabbit, "you're stuck."

"It all comes," said Pooh crossly, "of not having front doors big enough."

"It all comes," said Rabbit sternly, "of eating too much. I thought at the time," said Rabbit, "only I didn't like to say anything," said Rabbit, "that one of us was eating too much," said Rabbit, "and I knew it wasn't *me,*" he said. "Well, well, I shall go and fetch Christopher Robin."

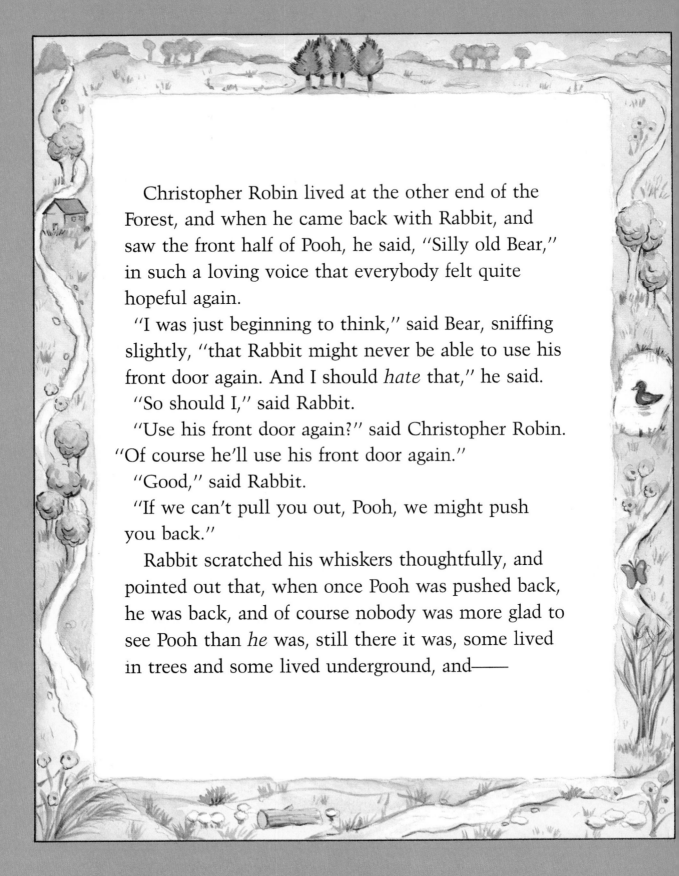

Christopher Robin lived at the other end of the Forest, and when he came back with Rabbit, and saw the front half of Pooh, he said, "Silly old Bear," in such a loving voice that everybody felt quite hopeful again.

"I was just beginning to think," said Bear, sniffing slightly, "that Rabbit might never be able to use his front door again. And I should *hate* that," he said.

"So should I," said Rabbit.

"Use his front door again?" said Christopher Robin. "Of course he'll use his front door again."

"Good," said Rabbit.

"If we can't pull you out, Pooh, we might push you back."

Rabbit scratched his whiskers thoughtfully, and pointed out that, when once Pooh was pushed back, he was back, and of course nobody was more glad to see Pooh than *he* was, still there it was, some lived in trees and some lived underground, and——

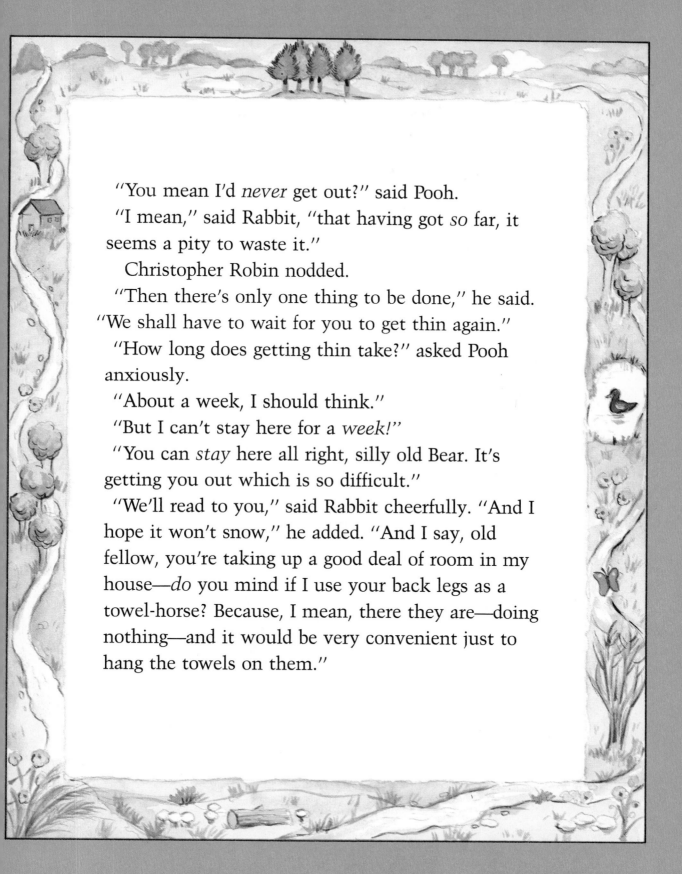

"You mean I'd *never* get out?" said Pooh.

"I mean," said Rabbit, "that having got *so* far, it seems a pity to waste it."

Christopher Robin nodded.

"Then there's only one thing to be done," he said. "We shall have to wait for you to get thin again."

"How long does getting thin take?" asked Pooh anxiously.

"About a week, I should think."

"But I can't stay here for a *week!*"

"You can *stay* here all right, silly old Bear. It's getting you out which is so difficult."

"We'll read to you," said Rabbit cheerfully. "And I hope it won't snow," he added. "And I say, old fellow, you're taking up a good deal of room in my house—*do* you mind if I use your back legs as a towel-horse? Because, I mean, there they are—doing nothing—and it would be very convenient just to hang the towels on them."

"A week!" said Pooh gloomily. *"What about meals?"*

"I'm afraid no meals," said Christopher Robin, "because of getting thin quicker. But we *will* read to you."

Bear began to sigh, and then found he couldn't because he was so tightly stuck; and a tear rolled down his eye, as he said:

"Then would you read a Sustaining Book, such as would help and comfort a Wedged Bear in Great Tightness?"

So for a week Christopher Robin read that sort of book at the North end of Pooh, and Rabbit hung his washing on the South end . . .

and in between Bear felt himself getting slenderer and slenderer. And at the end of the week Christopher Robin said, *"Now!"*

So he took hold of Pooh's front paws and Rabbit took hold of Christopher Robin, and all Rabbit's friends and relations took hold of Rabbit, and they all pulled together. . . .

And for a long time Pooh only said *"Ow!"* . . .

And *"Oh!"* . . .

And then, all of a sudden, he said *"Pop!"* just as if a cork were coming out of a bottle.

And Christopher Robin and
Rabbit and all Rabbit's friends and
relations went head-over-heels
backwards . . . and on the top of
them came Winnie-the-Pooh—
free!

So, with a nod of thanks to
his friends, he went on with his
walk through the forest, humming
proudly to himself. But,
Christopher Robin looked after
him lovingly, and said to himself,
"Silly old Bear!"

I. M. C.

# The King's Breakfast

by A. A. Milne

The King asked
The Queen, and
The Queen asked
The Dairymaid:
"Could we have some butter for
The Royal slice of bread?"
The Queen asked
The Dairymaid,
The Dairymaid
Said, "Certainly,
I'll go and tell
The cow
Now
Before she goes to bed."

The Dairymaid
She curtsied,
And went and told
The Alderney:
"Don't forget the butter for
The Royal slice of bread."

The Alderney
Said sleepily:
"You'd better tell
His Majesty
That many people nowadays
Like marmalade
Instead."

The Dairymaid
Said, "Fancy!"
And went to
Her Majesty
She curtsied to the Queen, and
She turned a little red:
"Excuse me,
Your Majesty,
For taking of
The liberty,
But marmalade is tasty, if
It's very
Thickly
Spread."

The Queen said,
"Oh!"
And went to
His Majesty:
"Talking of the butter for
The Royal slice of bread,
Many people
Think that
Marmalade
Is nicer.
Would you like to try a little
Marmalade
Instead?"

The King said,
"Bother!"
  And then he said,
"Oh, deary me!"
  The King sobbed, "Oh, deary me!"
  And went back to bed.
"Nobody,"
  He whimpered,
"Could call me
  A fussy man;
  I *only* want
  A little bit
  Of butter for
  My bread!"

The Queen said,
"There, there!"
And went to
The Dairymaid.
The Dairymaid
Said, "There, there!"
And went to the shed.
The cow said,
"There, there!
I didn't really
Mean it;
Here's milk for his porringer
And butter for his bread."

# LOOKING BACK

*See your Thinker's Handbook for tips.*

**Prewriting**

### Thinking and Writing About the Section

You've read about how the characters in this section figured out how to solve problems in all sorts of places. You can write a descriptive paragraph about one of the scenes to share with a partner. To begin, copy the chart and fill in the details.

| Scene | Descriptive details |
|---|---|
| Chameleon in a pickle jar | salty pickle juice |
| Lisa with her hurt friend | |
| Pooh stuck in the hole | |

**Writing**

Use the details in your chart to write a descriptive paragraph about one of the scenes to tell exactly how it looked. For more information on descriptive paragraphs, see your Writer's Handbook.

**Revising**

Read your first draft to a partner. Are there any details you can make more specific? Make changes, proofread, and write a final copy.

**Presenting**

Read your paragraph to a partner. Ask him or her to draw a picture of what you described.

## Books to Read

### Buford the Little Bighorn by Bill Peet

Buford, a mountain sheep, has to leave his home in the mountains because of his long horns. He fears for his life with every step he takes. One day he finds he can use his horns to get around in a really new way.

### Fox on Wheels by Edward Marshall

It seems Fox can't ever win. He's in a hurry to be in a bike race with his friends, but his mom wants him to do some shopping. Find out how Fox figures out how to shop *and* race at the same time.

### What Do You Do With a Kangaroo? by Mercer Mayer

First a kangaroo jumps in the window and onto your bed. Then a llama shows up, and a raccoon, a baby moose, a tiger, and a camel. One by one, they ask for something. What do you do? This will take some figuring out!

# Student's Handbooks

## Writer's Handbook

## Thinker's Handbook

## Word Study Handbook

## Glossary

This handbook answers questions you might ask yourself when you are writing. It will help you write the **Looking Back** assignments in this book as well as other writing assignments. It is divided into four parts: prewriting, writing, revising, and presenting. Each part tells about one step of the writing process. The handbook also explains these two types of writing: narrative and descriptive.

## Prewriting

### 1. I know the topic I'm going to write about, but how can I organize my ideas and narrow my topic?

One way is to use a chart, such as the one on page 131. Another way is to use a web, or cluster diagram. A cluster diagram shows at a glance how a main topic, subtopics, and details are related.

To make a cluster diagram, first write a main topic and circle it. Then write related subtopics around it. Circle them and draw lines to connect them to the main topic. Last, list details related to the subtopics.

Notice in the cluster diagram at the top of the next page that the main topic is *Cities: Old and New*. Coming out from the main topic are three narrower subtopics: *New York*, *Hub-Bub*, and *Boston*. The details that come from the subtopic *Hub-Bub* are more narrow still.

## 2. When I'm given a writing assignment, what is my first task?

When you receive a writing assignment, you should first decide on your *purpose* for writing and your *audience*. The people who will read your work are your audience. They may be your teacher, classmates, friends, family, or a writing partner. To determine your purpose, ask yourself: "What *type* of writing am I being asked to do?" Different types of writing have different purposes. Study the following chart to help you better understand your purpose for writing.

| Type of Writing | Purpose | Examples |
| --- | --- | --- |
| narrative | • to tell a story about something that happened to a real or make believe character<br>• to tell the events in the order in which they happened | • narrative paragraph<br>• personal experience narrative<br>• friendly letter |
| descriptive | • to paint a picture in words by using details that help the reader see, hear, feel, taste, or smell what you describe | • descriptive paragraph<br>• poem |

## Writing

### 1. Sometimes when I sit down, I just can't get started. What can I do then?

There are several ways to get started. Here are some suggestions.

<u>Review</u> Review what you did in Prewriting. Look for an idea that seems especially interesting. Use it in an opening paragraph.

<u>Tune Out</u> Tuning out means letting go of all other distractions. For many people, this means no TV, radio, food, or phone calls. Set yourself up in a place where you can concentrate. Then take time to focus on your writing alone.

<u>Push Ahead</u> Sit down and pick up a pencil. Push your ideas out of your head and get them down on paper.

### 2. What is a first draft?

A first draft is like a trial run. First drafts give you a chance to get your ideas down. The writing and spelling does not have to be perfect. In fact, write a first draft as freely as you can. Write whatever comes to mind on your subject. Don't stop writing and don't worry about perfect spelling, punctuation, or capitalization. If you stop to correct these kinds of errors, you may lose your train of thought.

## Revising

### 1. I have just written my first draft. What do I do next?

Take a minute to read over your first draft. "Listen" to yourself. Think about your big point. Is it clear? Will it make sense to your audience? Also ask yourself if your writing achieves the purpose you set. Have you really written the type of writing you were assigned? Does your draft reflect the steps in that kind of writing?

The chart below tells what can make each type of writing good.

| Type of Writing | What Makes It Good |
|---|---|
| narrative | • keeping to one main idea<br>• telling events in time order<br>• using signal words such as *first*, *next*, *then*, and *last*<br>• including all the events that are important to the story |
| descriptive | • keeping to one main idea<br>• choosing words that help the reader see, feel, hear, smell, or taste what you describe<br>• being sure the sentences support the main idea<br>• using colorful figures of speech |

## 2. What should I do when I revise?

First, revise your content. Have a writing conference with a small group, a partner, or your teacher. Read your draft aloud and ask what is good and what could be better. Take notes on the comments. They will help you make changes.

## 3. How do I make changes?

There are four kinds of changes to make when you revise: adding, taking out, reordering, and proofreading. Each one is explained below.

<u>Adding Information</u> Reread your draft. Check to see if you left out any important information. For example, does your narrative paragraph have all the important events?

<u>Taking Out Unnecessary Information</u> Check to see that you have kept to your topic. Take out any sentences that don't belong. Also check for unnecessary words. Can you say the same thing in fewer words?

<u>Moving Words, Sentences, and Paragraphs</u> The order of your words, sentences, and paragraphs is what makes your writing clear. Have you told things in the right order? You may need to move some words or sentences.

<u>Proofreading</u> Finally, check your paper for mistakes in spelling, punctuation, capitalization, and form. Use the proofreading marks at the top of the next page to help.

## Proofreader's Marks

| | | | |
|---|---|---|---|
| ☰ | Make a capital. | ℓ | Take out something. |
| ⊙ | Add a period. | ⌒→ | Move something. |
| ∧ | Add something. | ⊛ | Correct spelling. |

**4. How can I be sure I've done a thorough job of revising?**

You can use this Revision Checklist to check yourself.

## Revision Checklist

**Content**
- ✔ Did I say what I wanted to say?
- ✔ Are my details in order?
- ✔ Does my composition have a beginning, a middle, and an end?
- ✔ Is each paragraph about one main idea? Does the topic sentence state that main idea?
- ✔ Are any of the pronouns confusing?
- ✔ Have I taken out the unnecessary words?

**Mechanics**
- ✔ Does each sentence begin with a capital letter?
- ✔ Does each sentence end with the correct punctuation mark?
- ✔ Are other punctuation marks used correctly—such as commas and quotation marks?
- ✔ Do subjects and verbs agree?
- ✔ Did I keep the correct verb tense throughout?
- ✔ Did I capitalize proper nouns and adjectives?
- ✔ Did I check the spelling of difficult words?
- ✔ Is my handwriting clear and neat?

## Presenting

### 1. What are some ways I can present my writing to others?

Here are some suggestions.

<u>Read Aloud</u> Read your paper to your classmates or family. Use expression in your voice. Then invite feedback. Ask questions such as, "Could you predict how my story would end?"

<u>Make a Poster</u> Paste your paper to a large piece of poster board. Draw a picture to illustrate it. Hang it on the bulletin board in your classroom.

<u>Make a Book</u> You can make a book that contains your best writing. First draw a book cover on construction paper. Then place all the pages of your book together. Punch holes down the side. Weave yarn or thread through the holes and tie the ends. You can bring your book home to show your family or donate it to the school library.

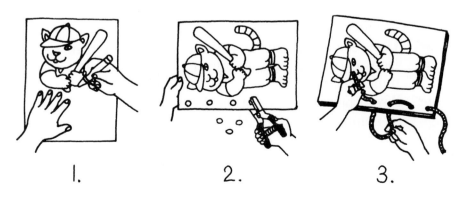

1.                    2.                    3.

## 2. How can our class work together to present our writing?

Here are some ways your class can work together.

<u>Start a Literary Magazine</u> Follow these steps:

a. As a class, think of a name for your magazine.

b. Ask for volunteers to type and copy the magazine.

c. Decide when and how often you will publish.

d. Choose a small group to be in charge of the magazine.

e. Along with your classmates, hand in the best examples of your writing. The magazine group will select what to include in each magazine issue.

<u>Have a Puppet Show</u> Follow these steps:

a. Rewrite one of your group stories as a play.

b. Help design and make a puppet for each part.

c. Put on the play, taking the part of the puppet you made.

d. Invite other classrooms to see your show.

<u>Display Your Work for the School</u> Ask your school principal if you and your classmates can display your work in the school lobby. Choose papers which are written about one specific topic. Help your group make a decorative border by drawing colorful pictures about the topic.

This handbook can help you with your work in *City Spaces*, in other classes, and outside of school. It can help you think through tasks before, during, and after you do them. The handbook also includes several activities that may make you think in new ways.

## Tips to Help You Think

### Task 1: Understanding Content

To better understand what you read, think about questions like these:

- Is what I'm reading making sense? Should I reread?

- Can I figure out why the characters are acting the way they are?

- Can I identify the character's goal or problem and how the character is trying to solve it?

- Can I make a prediction about what will happen?

- Could I put this difficult part in my own words?

- Can I state the point of this article?

- Would it help me to note causes, the order when things happen, or how they are alike or different?

- What main points do I need to include to talk about this article? What major events do I need to include to talk about this story?

## Task 2: Answering Questions

To *answer* questions, think about *asking* yourself questions such as these:

• Do I understand what this question is saying?

• Is this question asking for one or more answer?

• What other questions can I ask myself in order to lead up to this question?

• Would brainstorming for ideas help me get started?

• What do I need to do in order to get the answer to this kind of question?

| Examples of Questions | Ways to Answer |
|---|---|
| What is the topic? List three facts. | Recall information that was stated in the selection. |
| What happens in the story? What details support the main idea? | Gather and pull together several pieces of information. |
| What conclusion can you draw about the character? What can you figure out from these facts? | Make inferences by using clues and your common sense to lead you to a decision. |
| Why is this a good title? Do you like the story? Why? | Evaluate, or judge, what you read and give examples. |

### Task 3: Communicating Ideas

When you work with a partner or a small group, keep these questions in mind:

- Do we have a clear idea about what we are to do?

- How should we organize ourselves? Should we each take a job or work together in committees?

- How should we proceed? Should we ask questions, role-play, or do steps in order?

- Do we need to break down the major goal into smaller steps?

- Would it help to put our information in a chart or in a web?

- Do we need to take notes on our ideas?

- Are we keeping to the task, or are we getting away from it?

- Are we asking others to make their ideas clear?

- Can we repeat in our own words what others are saying so we know we understand each other?

- Have we completed our task? Did we do what we set out to do?

## Activities for You to Enjoy

### Activity 1: Solving Problems

One way to solve problems is to evaluate, or judge, information. Think about questions such as the following as you read the paragraph below. Tell what should be done to help Robin and Red Riding Hood.

- Do I have a clear idea of the overall problem in this situation?

- Would it help me to list each of the individual problems in this situation?

- How can I figure out which problems are the most serious?

- What solutions can I think of that could solve these problems?

- Can I predict what might happen for the solutions I suggest?

Red Riding Hood and her uncle Robin Hood have become lost on a journey through the woods. For several hours, they search for a way back to the forest path, but they only become tired and confused. Now it looks like it will rain. In one hour, it will be dark. Red and Robin will be stuck in the woods for the night. Each of them has a pack with some supplies. All together, they have some flint for making a fire, six arrows, some rope, one apple, and half of a loaf of bread. What should be done?

### Activity 2: Making Decisions

One way to make decisions is to think about your goal. Think about questions such as the ones below as you read the paragraph. Then help Peter decide what to do.

- Do I have a clear idea of the goal?

- Do I know what decisions the goal is leading me to make?

- Would it help me to picture in my mind what I need to do?

- Can I imagine what each decision would be like after I make it?

When Peter and his family went on a trip he started noticing all the signs that had no words but gave information, such as "Picnic Area." When he got home, he wanted to draw some signs to show the following things: Stay Out of My Room, Quiet! Kitten Asleep, Don't Touch My Tapes, I Love You, and I'm Sorry. He has all the paper, pens, and pencils he needs. Now it's time to get started and he needs to begin making decisions on how to picture his ideas.

## Activity 3: Asking the Right Questions

One way to ask the right kind of questions is to think about *why* you need to ask them. Read the tips below and use them to help Jessica ask the right questions.

- Think about your main purpose in asking questions.

- Decide which things are important for you to know.

- Think about information you already know and see if you can use it to ask what you don't know.

- Decide which questions will lead you to get the information you need.

Jessica loves playing baseball. She's an excellent pitcher. Jessica knows that there are several summer park teams, but she is not sure which one to join. Which of the following questions would be helpful to ask the team coaches?

What times are your practices?

How often do you practice?

Do you have team parties?

Who supplies the equipment for the team?

What is your win/loss record?

What color are your uniforms?

Does your team need a pitcher?

## Activity 4: Determining Relevance of Information

One way to determine the relevance of information is to figure out if it is relevant—necessary to your task—or irrelevant—not necessary or helpful. Read these questions and use them to help Detective Moto.

- Can I identify the task?

- Would it help me to list all the requirements?

- Can I trace where each piece of information might take me in order to figure out if it is relevant?

- Can I list the information that is not relevant?

- Can I explain what information is relevant?

Pat Moto, the famous dog detective, was asked to investigate the disappearance of the famous movie star dog, Sassy. These are the notes he wrote in his notebook.

last seen on movie set at 10:00 P.M.
is worth a million dollars
only eats Boney dog food
has a thick coat of golden fur
looks cute when it sleeps
disliked by director who is allergic to dog hair
is nice to have as a pet

Pat thinks some of this information is helpful. Which pieces of information are relevant?

On the next few pages are some of the strategies you've learned to figure out the meaning and pronunciation of words.

## Phonics: Consonant Sounds and Letters

Strategy 1: I can use what I know about **consonant sounds and letters** at the beginning, middle, and end of a word.

| Say these words: | | |
|---|---|---|
| view | offer | coax |
| bolt | juggle | ruin |
| toe | desert | board |
| calm | gallop | squirm |

## *Vocabulary and Skill Application*

Write the sentences. Use the words from the box to complete the sentences.

1. We had fun riding in the hot _____.
2. We had a great _____ of the land.
3. It looked like rain might _____ our riding trip.
4. A lightning _____ came down from the sky.
5. We tried to keep our horses _____.
6. I hit my horse with the _____ of my boot.
7. We didn't have to _____ the other horses to run.
8. We rode off at a fast _____ toward the mountains.

## Phonics: Blends and Digraphs

Strategy 2: I can use what I know about **blends and digraphs** at the beginning and end of a word.

---

Say these words. Listen to the sounds of the letters blended together or the letters that stand for one sound at the beginning or end of each word.

| | | | |
|---|---|---|---|
| **cr**ew | te**nd** | **ch**oke | wor**th** |
| **str**ay | sul**k** | **sh**all | tou**gh** |
| **fl**ight | chil**d** | **sh**ook | sear**ch** |

---

### *Vocabulary and Skill Application*

Write the sentences. Use the words from the box to complete the sentences.

1. Dan found a ____ puppy today.
2. Its little body ____ from the cold.
3. He thought the puppy would be ____ keeping.
4. The next day we had to ____ for the puppy.
5. Dan started to ____ because it had run away.
6. It was ____, but we found the puppy.
7. Mom said the puppy was acting just like a ____.
8. Dan would have to ____ to the puppy each day.

### *Phonics: Consonants and Context*

Strategy 3: I can use what I know about **consonants and context.**

Skill Lesson: Using Sense and Consonants on pages 207–208.

## Phonics: Short Vowel Sounds

Strategy 4: I can use what I know about **short vowel sounds.**

---

Say these words. Listen to the vowel sounds. What kind of letters are before and after the vowel in each word?

| Short *a* | Short *e* | Short *i* | Short *o* | Short *u* |
|-----------|-----------|-----------|-----------|-----------|
| fat | men | thick | doll | fun |
| past | tend | dizzy | flop | mud |
| fast | dread | drink | knot | buck |
| shall | spread | sprint | stop | judge |
| hatch | strength | string | shock | sculpt |

---

## *Vocabulary and Skill Application*

Write the sentences. Use the words from the box to complete the sentences.

1. I ran very ____.
2. There were several other ____ behind me.
3. We ran around a corner ____ a crowd of people.
4. I didn't have very much ____ left in my legs.
5. I was beginning to ____ the end of the race.
6. Pain started to ____ through my leg.
7. I was feeling ____ and tired.
8. Then, I knew I'd have to ____ the last few miles.
9. I sprinted the last few miles through some ____.
10. I didn't ____until I crossed the finish line.
11. The ____ said I was the winner of the race.

## Phonics: Long Vowel Sounds

Strategy 5: I can use what I know about **long vowel sounds.**

---

Say these words. Listen to the vowel sounds. Which words have two vowels together that stand for a long vowel sound? Which words have a vowel and a consonant followed by the letter *e*?

| Long *a* | Long *e* | Long *o* | Long *i* | Long *u* |
|----------|----------|----------|----------|----------|
| day      | need     | zone     | ice      | rule     |
| case     | peek     | coax     | while    | tube     |
| stray    | chief    | home     | light    | chute    |
| weigh    | squeal   | choke    | flight   | truce    |

---

## *Vocabulary and Skill Application*

Write the sentences. Use the words from the box to complete the sentences.

1. My favorite TV show came on during the _____.
2. The _____ of police talked about safety.
3. I drank a glass of _____ water _____ I watched.
4. Suddenly, I started to _____.
5. I let out a high _____.
6. My mom tried to _____ me to calm down.
7. She remembered the _____ about what to do.
8. Mom turned on the ceiling _____.
9. She took a _____ down my throat.
10. Mom looked in _____ there was something there.
11. "You _____ to be more careful!" said Mom.
12. Mom and I were both glad we had been at _____.

## Phonics: r-controlled Vowels

Strategy 6: I can use what I know about **r-controlled vowels.**

---

Say these words. Listen to the vowel sounds. What letter comes after the vowel in each word?

| | | | | |
|---|---|---|---|---|
| ma**r**k | he**r**d | sti**r** | co**r**d | cu**r**l |
| sta**r**t | ge**r**m | fi**r**m | sho**r**t | hu**r**t |
| pa**r**ty | we**r**e | shi**r**t | to**r**n | tu**r**n |
| sta**r**ve | pe**r**ch | fi**r**st | no**r**th | hu**r**dle |
| pa**r**don | ste**r**nly | squi**r**m | spo**r**t | pu**r**ple |

---

## *Vocabulary and Skill Application*

Write the sentences. Use the words from the box to complete the sentences.

1. Kris did not get a good _____ on her paper.
2. Mrs. Jones looked _____ at Kris.
3. Kris started to _____ in her chair.
4. She had wanted to _____ in a good paper.
5. She knew her paper was too _____.
6. Now she would not be able to go to Ted's _____.
7. All her friends _____ going to be there.
8. She was _____ and angry with herself.
9. Why hadn't she done a good job the _____ time.
10. Kris stayed home and wrote about the color _____.
11. Kris got off to a slow _____, but she wrote a good paper.

## Phonics: Vowel Sounds

Strategy 7: I can use what I know about **vowel sounds.**

---

Say these words. Listen to the vowel sounds. What letters stand for the vowel sound in each word?

| | | |
|---|---|---|
| f**ou**l | b**ow** | j**oi**n |
| b**ou**nce | sh**ow** | r**oy**al |
| th**ou**ght | fr**ow**n | en**joy** |
| m**ou**ntain | all**ow** | p**oi**son |

---

### *Vocabulary and Skill Application*

Write the sentences. Use the words from the box to complete the sentences.

1. I read a story about a ____ family.
2. They lived on a high ____ in a grand castle.
3. They would ____ people to visit their home.
4. They ____ this would make people happy.
5. The family wanted the people to ____ themselves.
6. They would put on a ____ for the people.
7. A clown would juggle and ____ balls.
8. A man would make believe he took ____ and fall.
9. Then, he would stand up and ____ to the king.
10. Everyone laughed and wanted to ____ in the fun.

## Structure: Syllabication

Strategy 8: I can use what I know about **syllabication.**

---

**A.** When a word ends in *-le*, divide before the consonant: jun·gle, hur·dle

**B.** When a word has two consonants between two vowels, divide the two consonants:
sur·round, can·yon

**C.** When a word has one consonant between two vowels, divide before or after the consonant:
o·bey, mod·ern

---

## *Vocabulary and Skill Application*

Write the sentences. Use the words from the list to complete the sentences.

| | | | | |
|---|---|---|---|---|
| offer | ballet | tiger | below | unique |
| pardon | traffic | talent | dozen | wander |
| juggle | respect | mantel | invent | silence |

1. Sandy has a special _____ in dance.
2. She likes to _____ new dance steps.
3. Her dance steps are _____ and interesting.
4. Sandy can do a _____ turns without stopping.
5. Sometimes she dances to music like a wild _____.
6. At other times she dances in complete _____.
7. Sandy wants to be the best _____ dancer ever.
8. The ballet teacher has great _____ for her talent.
9. Sandy hopes she will get an _____ to dance on TV.

## Structure: Prefixes and Suffixes

Strategy 9: I can use what I know about **prefixes and suffixes**

---

**A.** Add the prefix *mis-*    mis + *judge* = **mis***judge*
**B.** Add the prefix *pre-*    pre + *view* = **pre***view*
**C.** Add the prefix *dis-*    dis + *agree* = **dis***agree*

---

**A.** Add the suffixes -less and -able without changing the root word:
   *worth* + **less** = *worth***less**
   *reason* + **able** = *reason***able**
**B.** Drop the *e* and add the suffix *-ous:*
    *nerve* + **ous** = *nerv***ous**
**C.** Change the *y* to *i* and add the suffix *-ous:*
    *glory* + **ous** = *glori***ous**

---

## *Vocabulary and Skill Application*

Write the sentences. Use the words from the list to complete the sentences.

| | | | |
|---|---|---|---|
| nervous | preview | discourage | misunderstand |
| glorious | careless | reasonable | dangerous |

**1.** My parents try to ____ me from eating too much.
**2.** They don't want me to be ____ when I eat.
**3.** I know that eating too much can be ____.
**4.** I am very ____ and eat just what I need.

## Word Study: Dictionary

Strategy 10: I can use the **dictionary.**

**See Skill Lesson: Using a Dictionary or Glossary on pages 95–98.**

# Glossary

## How to Use the Pronunciation Key

After each entry word in this glossary, there is a special spelling, called the **pronunciation.** It shows how to say the word. The word is broken into syllables and then spelled with letters and signs. You can look up these letters and signs in the **pronunciation key** to see what sounds they stand for.

This dark mark (´) is called the **primary accent.** It follows the syllable you say with the most force. This lighter mark (ˈ) is the **secondary accent.** Say the syllable it follows with medium force. Syllables without marks are said with least force.

## Full Pronunciation Key

| | | | | | | | |
|---|---|---|---|---|---|---|---|
| **a** | hat, cap | **i** | it, pin | **p** | paper, cup | **ə** | stands for: |
| **ā** | age, face | **ī** | ice, five | **r** | run, try | | a in about |
| **ä** | father, far | | | **s** | say, yes | | e in taken |
| | | **j** | jam, enjoy | **sh** | she, rush | | i in pencil |
| **b** | bad, rob | **k** | kind, seek | **t** | tell, it | | o in lemon |
| **ch** | child, much | **l** | land, coal | **th** | thin, both | | u in circus |
| **d** | did, red | **m** | me, am | **ŦH** | then, smooth | | |
| | | **n** | no, in | | | | |
| **e** | let, best | **ng** | long, bring | **u** | cup, butter | | |
| **ē** | equal, be | | | **u̇** | full, put | | |
| **ėr** | her, learn | **o** | hot, rock | **ü** | rule, move | | |
| | | **ō** | open, go | | | | |
| **f** | fat, if | **ô** | order, all | **v** | very, save | | |
| **g** | go, bag | **oi** | oil, toy | **w** | will, woman | | |
| **h** | he, how | **ou** | house, out | **y** | young, yet | | |
| | | | | **z** | zoo, breeze | | |
| | | | | **zh** | measure, seizure | | |

**adobe**

**aquarium**

**balcony**

**baton**

# A

**ache** (āk), **1** a steady pain: *a stomach ache.* **2** have a steady pain: *My tooth aches.* 1 *noun,* 2 *verb,* **ached, ach·ing.**

**ad·mire** (ad mīr′), **1** look at or think of with wonder or pleasure: *We all admired the beautiful painting.* **2** think highly of; respect: *Everyone admired the explorer's courage. verb,* **ad·mired, ad·mir·ing.**

**a·do·be** (ə dō′bē), **1** brick made of clay baked in the sun. **2** built or made of adobe. See picture. 1 *noun,* 2 *adjective.*

**a·dult** (ə dult′ *or* ad′ult), **1** full-grown; grown-up; having full size and strength: *an adult person.* **2** a grown-up person. 1 *adjective,* 2 *noun.*

**ad·ver·tise·ment** (ad′vər tīz′mənt *or* ad vėr′tis mənt), public announcement; printed notice: *The furniture store has an advertisement in the newspaper of a special sale. noun.*

**a·maze** (ə māz′), surprise greatly; feel sudden wonder: *She was amazed at how much noise there was in the city. verb,* **a·mazed, a·maz·ing.**

**an·y·one** (en′ē wun), any person; anybody: *Can anyone go to this movie or is it just for adults? pronoun.*

**an·y·way** (en′ē wā), in any case: *I am coming anyway, no matter what you say. adverb.*

**a·part·ment** (ə pärt′mənt), room or group of rooms to live in; flat: *Our apartment is on the second floor of that building. noun.*

**a·quar·i·um** (ə kwer′ē əm), **1** tank or glass bowl in which living fish, other water animals, and water plants are kept. **2** building used for showing collections of living fish, water animals, and water plants. See picture. *noun.*

**ar·tis·tic** (är tis′tik), **1** of art or artists: *Our museum has many artistic works.* **2** to do with skill and good taste: *The card he chose shows he has artistic tastes.* **3** having good color and shapes: *artistic rug.* **4** having or showing an understanding of what is beautiful: *artistic tastes. adjective.*

**as·sist·ant** (ə sis′tənt), helper; aid: *I was her assistant in the library. noun.*

**as·tro·naut** (as′trə nôt), pilot or member of the crew of a spacecraft. *noun.*

# B

**bal·ance** (bal′əns), **1** instrument for weighing. **2** put or keep in a steady condition or position: *Can you balance a coin on its edge?* 1 *noun,* 2 *verb,* **bal·anced, bal·anc·ing.**

**bal·co·ny** (bal′kə nē), **1** a large outside ledge enclosed by a railing that juts out from an upper floor of a building. **2** an upper floor that juts out in a theater or hall, with seats for part of the audience. See picture. *noun, plural* **bal·co·nies.**

**ba·ton** (ba ton′), **1** the stick used by the leader of an orchestra, chorus, or band for beating time to the music. **2** stick handed to the next runner in a relay race. See picture. *noun.*

**bat·ter·y** (bat′ər ē), **1** a single electric cell: *Most flashlights work on two batteries.* **2** set of two or more electric cells that produce electric current. Batteries provide the current that starts car and truck engines. *noun, plural* **bat·ter·ies.**

**board** (bôrd), **1** a flat, wide piece of wood used to build something. **2** cover with such pieces of wood: *We board up the windows of the house in the fall.* **3** to get a room and meals for pay: *You will have to board somewhere else.* **4** a group of people who manage something: *a school* board. **5** to get on (a ship, train, bus, or plane): *We board the school bus at the corner.* 1,4 *noun* 2,3,5, *verb.*

**bolt** (bōlt), **1** a special kind of lock for a gate or door. **2** long streak of lightning. See picture. **3** roll of cloth. **4** to close with a bolt: *Bolt the doors.* **5** to suddenly rush away: *The horse bolted at the sound of the train.* 1,2,3 *noun,* 4,5 *verb.*

**bounce** (bouns), **1** spring into the air like a ball: *The baby likes to bounce up and down on the bed.* **2** cause to bounce: *Bounce the ball to me.* **3** bound; spring: *I caught the ball on the first bounce.* 1,2 *verb,* **bounced, bounc·ing;** 3 *noun.*

**breath** (breth), **1** the air drawn into and forced out of the lungs. **2** breathing: *Hold your breath a moment.* **3** small cloud in the air when a person breathes out: *You can see your breath on a very cold day.* **4** ability to breathe easily: *Running so fast made me lose my breath.* **5** slight movement in the air: *Not a breath was stirring. noun.*

**breathe** (brēᴛʜ), **1** draw air into the lungs and force it out. **2** stop for breath; stop to rest after hard work or exercise: *Let's take a minute to breathe before we begin again.* **3** say softly: *Don't breathe a word of this to anyone. verb,* **breathed, breath·ing.**

**buck** (buk), **1** a male deer, goat, hare, or rabbit. **2** jump into the air with the back curved and come down with the front legs stiff: *My horse began to buck, but I managed to stay on.* 1 *noun,* 2 *verb,* **bucked, buck·ing.**

**busi·ness** (biz′nis), **1** thing that one is busy at; work; occupation: *A carpenter's business is building.* **2** matter; affair: *I am tired of the whole business.* **3** buying and selling; trade: *This hardware store does a big business in tools.* **4** a store, factory, or other way of making money: *They sold the bakery business. noun, plural* **busi·ness·es** for 4.

# C

**calm** (käm *or* kälm), **1** quiet; still; not stormy or windy: *In fair weather, the sea is usually calm.* **2** not stirred up; peaceful: *Although she was frightened, she answered with a calm voice.* **3** quietness; stillness: *There was a sudden calm as the wind dropped.* **4** make or become calm: *The crying baby soon calmed down.* 1,2 *adjective,* 3 *noun,* 4 *verb,* **calm, calm·ing.**

**can·yon** (kan′yən), a narrow valley with high, steep sides, usually with a stream at the bottom. See picture. *noun.*

**car·a·van** (kar′ə van), **1** group of merchants, pilgrims, tourists or the like traveling together for safety through difficult or dangerous country: *A caravan of merchants and camels, carrying spices and silks, moved across the desert.* **2** a closed truck, trailer, or large covered wagon for moving people or goods; van. *noun.*

**case¹** (kās), some special state or time: *In case of fire, walk to the door. noun.*

**case²** (kās), **1** something that holds or covers: *Put your glasses in this case.* **2** a box: *There is a case of canned fruit in the basement. noun.*

**ceil·ing** (sē′ling), **1** the inside, top covering of a room. **2** distance between the earth and the lowest clouds: *The man on the radio said that the ceiling was only 300 feet. noun.*

**cel·e·bra·tion** (sel′ə brā′shən), **1** special services or activities in honor of a person, act, time, or day: *A Fourth of July celebration often has a fireworks display.* **2** act of celebrating: *celebration of a birthday. noun.*

**cel·lar** (sel′ər), underground room or rooms, usually under a building and often used for storing food or fuel. *noun.*

| a hat | oi oil | ə stands for: |
|---|---|---|
| ā age | ou out | a in about |
| ä far | u cup | e in taken |
| e let | ù put | i in pencil |
| ē equal | ü rule | o in lemon |
| ėr term | ch child | u in circus |
| i it | ng long | |
| ī ice | sh she | |
| o hot | th thin | |
| ō open | ᴛʜ then | |
| ô order | zh measure | |

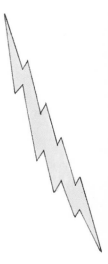

**bolt** of lightning

**canyon**

**chameleon**

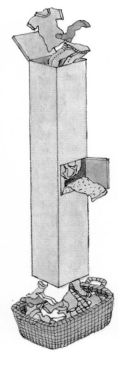

**chute**

**ce·ment** (sə ment′), **1** a fine, gray powder made by burning clay and limestone. Cement mixed with water, sand, and gravel becomes hard like stone when it dries. It is used to make sidewalks, streets, floors, and walls. **2** any soft material which, when it hardens, makes things stick together: *rubber cement. noun.*

**cha·me·le·on** (kə mē′lē ən), a small lizard that can change the color of its skin to blend with whatever is around it. See picture. *noun.*

**chief** (chēf), **1** head of a tribe or group; leader; person highest in rank or authority: *a chief of police.* **2** at the head; leading: *the chief engineer of a building project.* **3** most important; main: *the chief town in the county.* 1 *noun,* 2,3 *adjective.*

**chute** (shüt), a steep slide. There are chutes for carrying mail, dirty clothes, and coal to a lower level. See picture. *noun.*

**claw** (klô), **1** a sharp, hooked nail on a bird's or animal's foot. **2** scratch, tear, seize, or pull with claws or hands: *The kitten was clawing the screen door.* 1 *noun,* 2 *verb,* **clawed, claw·ing.**

**coax** (kōks), persuade by soft words; influence by pleasant ways: *She coaxed me into letting her use my bike. verb,* **coaxed, coax·ing.**

**com·mand** (kə mand′), **1** give an order to; order: *The king commanded the ship to sail at once.* **2** to be the head of: *The sailor commanded his ship.* **3** to deserve and to get: *When there is little food, it commands a lot of money.* **4** to be able to have and to use: *I cannot command that much money.* **5** order: *The sailor obeyed the king's command.* 1,2,3,4 *verb,* 5 *noun.*

**com·pe·ti·tion** (kom′pə tish′ən), **1** trying hard to win or gain something: *There is competition in many games.* **2** contest: *They won the music competition. noun.*

**com·plain** (kəm plān′), **1** say that something is wrong; find fault: *We complained that the room was cold.* **2** talk about one's pain or troubles: *He is always complaining about his health.* **3** accuse or charge: *I complained to the police about the barking of my neighbor's dog. verb,* **com·plained, com·plain·ing.**

**com·pli·cate** (kom′plə kāt), **1** make hard to understand or to settle; mix up; confuse: *Too many rules complicate a game.* **2** make worse or more mixed up: *Headaches can be complicated by eye trouble. verb,* **com·pli·cat·ed, com·pli·cat·ing.**

**con·cen·trate** (kon′sən trāt), **1** bring or come together in one place: *The audience at the theater concentrated around the stage.* **2** pay close attention: *I concentrated on my reading so I would understand the story.* **3** make stronger: *To concentrate orange juice, you need to take the water away. verb,* **con·cen·trat·ed, con·cen·trat·ing.**

**con·densed milk** (kən densd′ milk′), a thick, sweet, canned milk, made when some of the water in regular milk is dried off. *noun.*

**con·tam·i·nate** (kən tam′ə nāt), make something dirty or unhealthy by touching it: *The water was contaminated by garbage. verb,* **con·tam·i·nat·ed, con·tam·i·nat·ing.**

**con·ven·ient** (kən vē′nyənt), **1** saving trouble; well arranged; easy to use: *take a convenient bus.* **2** easily done; not troublesome: *Will it be convenient for you to bring your lunch to school? adjective.*

**cop·per·y** (kop′ər ē), reddish brown: *She had coppery hair. adjective.*

**cot·ton·wood** (kot′n wůd′), **1** a kind of American poplar tree with tufts that look like cotton on its seeds. **2** the soft wood of this tree. *noun.*

**cour·age** (kėr′ij), bravery; meeting danger without fear. *noun.*

**crea·ture** (krē′chər), **1** any living person or animal. **2** anything that is created: *Ghosts are creatures of the mind. noun.*

**crew** (krü), **1** the sailors needed to do the work on a ship, or to row a boat. **2** group of persons working aboard an aircraft. **3** any group of people working or acting together: *A train crew runs a railroad train. noun.*

**crim·son** (krim′zən), **1** deep red. **2** turn deep red in color: *The child's face crimsoned after he fell down.* **1** *adjective,* **2** *verb,* **crim·soned, crim·son·ing.**

**cross·ly** (krôs′lē), in a bad temper; complaining: *He answered crossly because he didn't feel well. adverb.*

**cur·tain** (kėrt′n), **1** cloth hung at windows or in doors to protect a room from cold or to decorate it. See picture. **2** a hanging screen which separates the stage of a theater from the part where the audience sits. *noun.*

# D

**dare** (der *or* dar), **1** be bold: *The children dared to explore the haunted house.* **2** have courage to try; not be afraid of: *The pioneers dared the dangers of a strange land.* **3** challenge: *I dare you to jump the puddle.* **4** a challenge: *I took his dare to jump.* **1-3** *verb,* **dared, dar·ing;** **4** *noun.*

**daugh·ter** (dô′tər), female child. A girl is the daughter of her father and mother. *noun.*

**dec·o·rate** (dek′ə rāt′), **1** make beautiful; trim; adorn: *We decorated the parade float.* **2** paint or paper (a room): *The old rooms looked like new after they had been decorated.* **3** give a badge, ribbon, or medal to. *verb,* **dec·o·rat·ed, dec·o·rat·ing.**

**del·i·cate** (del′ə kit), **1** pleasing to the taste; mild or soft: *delicate foods, delicate colors.* **2** of fine weave,

quality, or make; thin; easily torn: *A spider web is very delicate. adjective.*

**de·liv·er** (di liv′ər), **1** carry and give out: *The girl delivers newspapers.* **2** give up; hand over: *He delivered the birthday present. verb,* **de·liv·ered, de·liv·er·ing.**

**des·ert** (dez′ərt), **1** region without water and trees. It is usually sandy. There is a great desert in the northern part of Africa. See picture. **2** not inhabited or cultivated; wild: *They were stranded on a desert island.* **1** *noun,* **2** *adjective.*

**de·serve** (di zėrv′), have a right to; have a claim to; be worthy of: *A hard worker deserves good pay. verb,* **de·served, de·serv·ing.**

**dif·fer·ence** (dif′ər əns), **1** not being alike: *There is a great difference between night and day.* **2** what is left after subtracting one number from another: *The difference between 15 and 7 is 8. noun.*

**dif·fi·cult** (dif′ə kult), **1** hard to do or understand: *Arithmetic is difficult for some pupils.* **2** hard to get along with; not easy to please: *My cousins are difficult and always want their own way. adjective.*

**di·rect·ly** (də rekt′lē *or* di rekt′le), **1** in a direct line or manner; straight: *This road runs directly into the center of town.* **2** at once; right away: *Come home directly! adverb.*

**dis·cour·age** (dis kėr′ij), **1** take away the courage of; destroy the hopes of: *Failing again and again discourages anyone.* **2** try to prevent by disapproving; frown upon: *All her friends discouraged her from such a dangerous swim. verb,* **dis·cour·aged, dis·cour·ag·ing.**

**dis·tance** (dis′təns), **1** space in between: *The distance from the farm to the town is five miles.* **2** place far away: *She saw a light in the distance. noun.*

| a hat | oi oil | ə stands for: |
|---|---|---|
| ā age | ou out | a in about |
| ä far | u cup | e in taken |
| e let | ů put | i in pencil |
| ē equal | ü rule | o in lemon |
| ėr term | ch child | u in circus |
| i it | ng long | |
| ī ice | sh she | |
| o hot | th thin | |
| ō open | ᴛʜ then | |
| ô order | zh measure | |

**curtain**

**desert**

**379**

**di·vorce** (də vôrs′), **1** end a marriage: *The judge divorced Mr. and Mrs. Jones.* **2** separate: *In sports, exercise and play are not divorced.* 1 *noun*, 2 *verb*, **di·vorced, di·vorc·ing.**

**doc·tor** (dok′tər), **1** person who knows how to make sick people better. **2** treat sickness in: *My mother doctored me when I had a cold.* 1 *noun*, 2 *verb*, **doc·tored, doc·tor·ing.**

**doz·en** (duz′n), 12; group of 12: *We will need three dozen eggs and a dozen rolls.* *noun, plural* **doz·ens** or (after a number) **doz·en.**

**dread** (dred), **1** fear greatly (what is to come); dislike to experience: *I dreaded my visits to the dentist. Cats dread water.* **2** dreaded; dreadful: *The dread day of the trial was near.* 1 *verb*, **dread·ed, dread·ing,** 2 *adjective.*

# E

**e·lec·tric·i·ty** (i lek′tris′ə tē), **1** form of energy which can produce light, heat, motion, and magnetism: *Electricity makes light bulbs shine, radios and televisions play, cars start, and subways run.* **2** electric current: *Most refrigerators are run by electricity. noun.*

**el·e·va·tor** (el′əvā′tər), **1** something which raises or lifts up. **2** a moving box or cage to carry people and things up and down in a building or mine. See picture. *noun.*

**en·er·gy** (en′ər jē), **1** will to work: *I was so full of energy that I could not keep still.* **2** power to work or act; force: *All our energies were used in keeping the fire from spreading.* **3** the ability for doing work, such as lifting or moving an object. Light, heat, and electricity are different forms of energy. *noun, plural* **en·er·gies.**

elevator

**es·pe·cial·ly** (e spesh′ə lē), more than others; chiefly: *His book is especially designed for students.* adverb.

**e·vent** (i vent′), **1** happening; important happening: *The discovery of America was a great event.* **2** item or contest in a program of sports: *Running a mile was the last event. noun.*

**ex·per·i·ment** (ek sper′ə ment *for 1;* ek sper′ə mənt *for 2*), **1** try in order to find out; make trials or tests: *Babies experiment with their hands.* **2** trial or test to find out something: *a cooking experiment. Scientists test out theories by experiment.* 1 *verb*, **ex·per·i·ment·ed ex·per·i·ment·ing,** 2 *noun.*

**ex·pert** (ek′spėrt′ *for 1;* ek spėrt′ *or* ek′spėrt′ *for 2*), **1** person who has much skill or who knows a great deal about some special thing: *She is an expert at fishing.* **2** having much skill; knowing a great deal about some special thing: *an expert painter.* 1 *noun*, 2 *adjective.*

# F

**fa·mous** (fā′məs), very well known; noted: *The famous singer was greeted by a large crowd. adjective.*

**fa·vor·ite** (fā′vər it), **1** liked better than others: *What is your favorite flower?* **2** the one liked better than others; person or thing liked very much: *He is a favorite with everybody.* 1 *adjective*, 2 *noun.*

**fetch** (fech), **1** go and get; bring: *Please fetch me my glasses.* **2** to make come: *Her call fetched me at once.* **3** be sold for: *These eggs will fetch a good price. verb.*

**for·ev·er** (fər ev′ər), **1** for ever; without ever coming to an end: *Nobody lives forever.* **2** always; all the time: *He seems to be forever complaining. adverb.*

**foul** (foul), **1** very dirty; nasty; smelly: *foul air.* **2** make dirty; become dirty; soil: *Oil fouled the harbor.* **3** unfair; against the rules. **4** (in football, basketball, and other sports) an unfair play; thing done against the rules. **5** unfavorable: *Foul weather delayed us.* **1,3,5** *adjective,* **2** *verb,* **fouled, foul·ing, 4** *noun.*

**fur·ni·ture** (fėr′nə chər), movable items needed in a room or house. Beds, chairs, tables, and desks are furniture. *noun.*

# G

**gal·ax·y** (gal′ək sē), group of billions of stars forming one system. Many galaxies outside our own can be seen with a telescope: *The earth and sun are part of one galaxy.* See picture. *noun, plural* **gal·ax·ies.**

**gath·er** (gaᴛн′ər), **1** collect; bring into one place: *He gathered his books and papers and left for school.* **2** come together: *A crowd gathered to hear the speech. verb,* **gath·ered, gath·er·ing.**

**gi·gan·tic** (jī gan′tik), big like a giant; huge: *An elephant is a giantic animal. adjective.*

**glare** (gler *or* glar), **1** a strong, unpleasant light; light that shines so brightly that it hurts the eyes. **2** shine strongly or unpleasantly; shine so brightly as to hurt the eyes. **3** a fierce, angry stare. **1,3** *noun,* **2** *verb,* **glared, glar·ing.**

**greet·ing** (grē′ting), **1** act or words of a person who greets somebody; welcome. **2** greeting, friendly wishes at a special time. *noun.*

# H

**hai·ku** (hī′kü), a poem of three lines and containing only 17 syllables. *noun, plural* **hai·ku.**

**herd** (hėrd), **1** group of animals of one kind, especially large animals, keeping, feeding, or moving together: *a herd of cows.* **2** a large number of people. **3** form into a flock, herd, or group: *The farmer herded the cows over to the barn door.* **1,2** *noun,* **3** *verb.*

**her·o·ine** (her′ō ən), a girl or woman admired for her bravery, great deeds, or noble qualities. *noun.*

**hip·po·pot·a·mus** (hip′ə pot′ə məs), a huge animal found in and near the rivers of Africa. Hippopotami eat plants and can stay under water for a long time. See picture. *noun, plural* **hip·po·pot·amus·es, hip·po·pot·a·mi.**

**hoot** (hüt), **1** the sound that an owl makes. **2** make this sound or one like it. **1** *noun,* **2** *verb,* **hoot·ed, hoot·ing.**

**hor·ri·ble** (hôr′ə bəl), causing horror; frightful; shocking: *a horrible crime. adjective.*

**hos·pi·tal** (hos′pi təl), place for the care of sick or hurt people. *noun.*

**ho·tel** (hō tel′), house or large building that supplies rooms and food for pay to travelers and others. *noun.*

**hur·dle** (hėr′dl), **1** something for people or horses to jump over in a race. **2** jump over: *The horse hurdled both the fence and the ditch.* **1** *noun,* **2** *verb,* **hur·dled, hur·dling.**

# I

**in·spec·tor** (in spek′ tər), **1** person who inspects. **2** officer appointed to inspect: *a milk inspector. noun.*

**in·vent** (in vent′), **1** make or think out (something new): *Alexander Graham Bell invented the telephone. verb.*

**i·ron** (ī′ərn), **1** a metal from which tools and machines are made: *A blacksmith makes horseshoes of iron.* **2** make of iron: *an iron box.* **3** an instrument that is heated and used to press clothing. **4** press with an iron: *I ironed two curtains.* **1,2,3** *noun,* **4** *verb.*

**is·land** (ī′lənd), a mass of land with water all around it. See picture. *noun.*

| a hat | oi oil | ə stands for: |
|---|---|---|
| ā age | ou out | a in about |
| ä far | u cup | e in taken |
| e let | ů put | i in pencil |
| ē equal | ü rule | o in lemon |
| ėr term | ch child | u in circus |
| i it | ng long | |
| ī ice | sh she | |
| o hot | th thin | |
| ō open | ᴛʜ then | |
| ô order | zh measure | |

**galaxy**

**hippopotamus**

**island**

# J

**jeal·ous** (jel′əs), fearful that somebody you love may love someone else better, or may prefer someone else to you: *The child was jealous when anyone paid attention to the new baby. adjective.*

**jour·ney** (jėr′nē), **1** traveling from one place to another; trip: *a journey around the world.* **2** travel; take a trip: *She journeyed to Europe last summer.* **1** *noun, plural* **jour·neys;** **2** *verb,* **jour·neyed, jour·ney·ing.**

**jug·gle** (jug′əl), **1** to do tricks that need skill in balancing or catching: *He juggled with knives by balancing them on his nose.* **2** do tricks with: *She can juggle three balls, keeping them all in the air at once.* **3** change by a trick: *The robber took money from the store by juggling its records. verb,* **jug·gled, jug·gling.**

**jun·gle** (jung′gəl), wild land where bushes, vines, and trees grow thickly together. *noun.*

kimono

# K

**ki·mo·no** (kə mō′nə), a loose garment held in place by a sash, worn by both men and women in Japan. See picture. *noun.*

**king·dom** (king′dəm), a country that is ruled by a king or queen; land or territory ruled by one king. *noun.*

# L

**lab·o·ra·to·ry** (lab′rə tôr′ē), place where scientific work is done: *a chemical laboratory. noun, plural* **lab·o·ra·to·ries.**

**lan·guage** (lang′gwij), **1** human speech, spoken or written: *A common language ties people together.* **2** the speech of one nation, tribe, or other large group of people: *the French language. noun.*

lasso

**lar·der** (lär′dər), **1** pantry; place where food is kept. **2** stock of food: *The hunter's larder included flour, bacon, and deer meat. noun.*

**las·so** (las′ō *or* la sü′), **1** a long rope with a noose at the end, used for catching horses and cattle. **2** catch with a lasso. See picture. *noun, plural* **las·sos** *or* **las·soes;** **2** *verb,* **las·soed, las·soing.**

**laun·dry** (lôn′drē), clothes washed or to be washed. *noun, plural* **laun·dries.**

**leap·frog** (lēp′frog′), game in which one player leaps over another who is bending over. *noun.*

**lie**[1] (lī), **1** something said that is not true: *His lie was discovered.* **2** say something that is not true: *Don't lie about it.* **1** *noun,* **2** *verb,* **lied, ly·ing.**

**lie**[2] (lī), have your body in a flat position; *I want to lie down. verb,* **lay, ly·ing.**

**lose** (lüz), **1** not to have any longer: *Try not to lose your key.* **2** not be able to find: *Did you lose a book?* **3** not win: *We may lose the game. verb,* **lost, los·ing.**

# M

**mag·nif·i·cent** (mag nif′ə sənt), richly colored or decorated; splendid: *a magnificent view of the mountains. adjective.*

**maj·es·ty** (maj′ə stē), a title given to a king or queen: *His Majesty, Her Majesty. noun, plural* **maj·es·ties.**

**man·a·ger** (man′ə jər), person who manages: *She is the manager of the department store. noun.*

**man·tel** (man′tl), **1** shelf above a fireplace: *We looked at the clock on the mantel. noun.*

**mar·vel·ous** (mär′və ləs), fine; excellent; splendid: *a marvelous time. adjective.*

**may·fly** (mā′flī), any of an order of slender insects having lacy forewings which are much larger than the back wings. Mayflies die soon after reaching the adult stage. See picture. *noun, plural* **may·flies.**

**med·i·cine** (med′ə sən), **1** science of treating, preventing, or curing diseases and improving health: *You must study medicine for several years before you can become a doctor.* **2** substance such as a drug, used to treat, prevent, or cure disease: *While I was sick I had to take my medicine two times a day. noun.*

**mes·sage** (mes′ij), words sent from one person to another: *a radio message. noun.*

**mes·sen·ger** (mes′n jər), person who carries a message or goes on an errand. *noun.*

**met·al** (met′l), **1** substance such as iron, gold, silver, copper, lead, and tin. **2** made of a metal, or a mixture of metals. See picture. 1 *noun,* 2 *adjective.*

**mil·lion** (mil′yən), one thousand thousands; 1,000,000. *noun, adjective.*

**mis·judge** (mis juj′), **1** judge wrongly: *I misjudged the distance to the next step, and tripped on the stairs.* **2** judge unjustly: *The teacher soon discovered that she had misjudged the girl's character. verb,* **mis·judged, mis·judg·ing.**

**mis·sion** (mish′ən), **1** to send or be sent on some special work: *He was sent on a mission to get the secret formula.* **2** persons sent out on some special business: *She was one of a mission sent to the king.* **3** home of a group of people who believe in the same idea: *She joined the mission that was helping people who had no money.* **4** a person's purpose in life: *Her mission was to help those in need. noun.*

**mod·ern** (mod′ərn), **1** of the present time; of times not long past: *color television is a modern invention.* **2** up-to-date; not old-fashioned: *modern views. adjective.*

**moss** (môs), very small, soft, green plants that grow close together like a carpet on the ground, on rocks, or on trees. *noun, plural* **moss·es.**

**moun·tain** (moun′tən), **1** a very high hill. **2** of or having something to do with mountains: *mountain air.* **3** a very large heap or pile of anything: *a mountain of rubbish.* See picture. 1,3 *noun,* 2 *adjective.*

# N

**ner·vous** (nėr′vəs), easily excited or upset: *A person who has been overworked is likely to become nervous. adjective.*

**noose** (nüs), loop with a slip knot that tightens as the string or rope is pulled. Nooses are used especially in lassos and snares. *noun.*

# O

**o·bey** (ō bā′), do what one is told to do: *The dog obeyed and went home.* **o·beyed, o·bey·ing** *verb.*

**of·fer** (ô′fər), **1** hold out to be taken or refused; present: *offer a gift.* **2** propose; suggest: *She offered a few ideas to improve the plan.* **3** act of offering: *an offer of money.* 1,2 *verb,* 3 *noun.*

**old-fash·ioned** (ōld′fash′ənd), **1** out-of-date; of an old style: *old-fashioned clothing.* **2** keeping to old ways or ideas: *My grandparents are quite old-fashioned. adjective.*

**or·i·ga·mi** (or′ə gä′mē), the Japanese art of folding paper to make objects such as figures of birds and flowers. *noun.*

**o·ver·alls** (ō′vər ôlz′), loose trousers with a piece covering the chest. Overalls are usually worn over clothes to keep them clean. *noun plural.*

| a hat | oi oil | ə stands for: |
|---|---|---|
| ā age | ou out | a in about |
| ä far | u cup | e in taken |
| e let | ů put | i in pencil |
| ē equal | ü rule | o in lemon |
| ėr term | ch child | u in circus |
| i it | ng long | |
| ī ice | sh she | |
| o hot | th thin | |
| ō open | ᴛʜ then | |
| ô order | zh measure | |

**mayfly**

**metal pot**

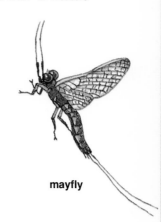

**mountain**

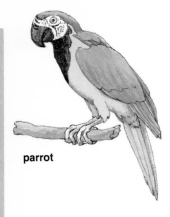

**parrot**

**peninsula**
Florida is a **peninsula.**

**pigeon**

**possum**

# P

**pack·age** (pak′ij), **1** bundle of things packed or wrapped together. **2** put in a package or wrapper: *Food stores package some fruits and vegetables.* 1 *noun,* 2 *verb,* **pack·aged, pack·ag·ing.**

**pa·ja·mas** (pə jä′məz *or* pə jam′əz), clothes to sleep in, made up of a shirt and loose trousers. *noun plural.*

**par·ent** (per′ənt *or* par′ ənt), **1** father or mother. **2** to make happen: *Too little work can be the parent of bad grades. noun.*

**par·lor** (pär′lər), **1** room for receiving or entertaining guests; sitting room. **2** a decorated room used as a shop; shop: *a beauty parlor. noun.*

**par·rot** (par′ət), bird with a stout, hooked bill and often with bright-colored feathers. Some parrots can imitate sounds and repeat words and sentences. See picture. *noun.*

**pa·tience** (pā′shəns), **1** calm bearing of pain, or waiting, or of anything that annoys, troubles, or hurts: *The cat watched the mouse hole with patience.* **2** long, hard work; steady effort. *noun.*

**pause** (pôz), **1** stop for a time; wait: *I paused for a moment to look in a store window.* **2** a brief stop or rest: *After a pause for lunch we returned to work.* 1 *verb,* **paused, paus·ing;** 2 *noun.*

**pay·load** (pā′lōd′), **1** the load carried by an aircraft, train, truck, etc., which can be sold. **2** the cargo of a rocket, including passengers and instruments. 1,2 *noun.*

**pen·guin** (pen′gwin), a sea bird with flippers for diving and swimming in place of wings for flying. Penguins live in Antarctica and other cold areas. *noun.*

**pen·nin·su·la** (pə nin′sə lə), piece of land almost surrounded by water, or extending far out into the water. See picture. *noun.*

**pho·to·graph** (fō′tə graf), **1** picture made with a camera. **2** take a photograph of. 1 *noun,* 2 *verb.*

**pig·eon** (pij′ən), bird with a plump body and short legs; dove. See picture. *noun.*

**pi·lot** (pi′lət), **1** a person whose business is to steer a ship or an airplane. **2** act as a pilot of; steer: *She piloted the ship up the river.* 1 *noun,* 2 *verb,* **pi·lot·ed, pi·lot·ing.**

**pit·y** (pit′ē), **1** the feeling of being sorry for someone in trouble or pain. **2** feel pity for: *I pitied the sobbing child.* **3** thing to be sorry for: *It is a pity to be kept in the house in good weather.* 1,3 *noun, plural* **pit·ies,** 2 *verb,* **pit·ied, pit·y·ing.**

**piz·za** (pēt′sə), a spicy Italian dish made by baking a large flat layer of bread dough covered with cheese, tomato sauce, herbs, and other things. *noun.*

**plaque** (plak), a thin flat plate or tablet usually used as a wall decoration. *noun.*

**poi·son** (poi′zn), **1** a substance that is very dangerous to life and health when it is breathed or swallowed. Arsenic and lead are poisons. **2** kill or harm by poison. **3** put poison in or on: *poison food.* 1 *noun,* 2,3 *verb.*

**po·lite** (pə līt′), behaving properly; having or showing good manners: *The polite girl gave the old man her seat on the bus. adjective.*

**pos·sum** (pos′əm), a small animal that lives in trees and carries its young in a pocket. When it is caught, it plays dead. A possom is often called an opossum. See picture. *noun, plural* **pos·sums** *or* **pos·sum.**

**post card** (pōst′ card), card about $3\frac{1}{2}$ by $5\frac{1}{2}$ inches for sending a message by mail. Some postcards have pictures on one side. *noun.*

**prair·ie** (prer′ē), a large area of level or rolling land with grass but few or no trees. *noun.*

**pres·i·dent** (prez′ə dənt), **1** the chief officer of a company, college, society, or club. **2** President, the person elected to run a country. *noun.*

**pur·pose** (pėr′pəs), a plan; aim; intention; something one has in mind to get or do: *Her purpose in coming to see us was to ask for a donation to the hospital fund.* noun.

# Q

**qual·i·fy** (kwol′ə fī), **1** made fit or able to do something: *Can you qualify yourself for the job?* **2** become fit, show oneself fit: *He qualified for a driver's license.* verb, **qual·i·fied, qual·i·fy·ing.**

**quiz** (kwiz), **1** a short or informal test: *Each week the teacher gives us a quiz in spelling.* **2** examine by questions; test the knowledge of. 1 noun, plural **quiz·zes;** 2 verb, **quizzed, quiz·zing.**

# R

**ra·dio** (rā′dē ō), **1** a way of sending and receiving sounds through the air: *The pilot talked to us by radio.* **2** an instrument for hearing these sounds: *He got a radio for his birthday.* **3** of radio: *a radio station, a radio program.* See picture. 1,2 noun, 3 adjective.

**rea·son** (rē′zn), **1** cause: *I have my reasons for doing it this way.* **2** explanation: *What is your reason for being so late?* **3** think things out; solve new problems: *Most animals can't reason.* 1,2 noun, 3 verb, **rea·soned, rea·son·ing.**

**re·cess** (rē′ses *or* ri ses′ *for 1,3;* ri ses′ *for 2*), **1** time during which work stops: *Our school has an hour's recess at noon.* **2** take a recess: *The committee recessed for lunch.* **3** part of a wall or other flat surface set back from the rest: *The bench was in the recess of the wall.* 1,3 noun, 2 verb, **re·cessed, re·cess·ing.**

**re·lay race** (rē′lā rās) race in which each member of a team runs, swims, or moves in some other way through only a certain part of the distance. noun.

**re·li·a·ble** (ri lī′ə bəl), worthy of trust; able to be depended on: *Send her to the bank for the money; she is reliable.* adjective.

**re·spect** (ri spekt′) **1** show special attention to: *We respect a kind person.* **2** the act of respecting: *This teacher has the respect of his class.* 1 verb, **re·spect·ed, re·spect·ing;** 2 noun.

**res·taur·ant** (res′tər ənt *or* res′tə ränt′), place to buy and eat a meal. See picture. noun.

**re·tire** (ri tīr′), **1** give up an office or occupation: *Our teachers retire at 65.* **2** remove from an office or occupation. **3** go away, especially to a place which is more quiet or private: *They retired to the country.* **4** go to bed: *We retire early.* verb, **re·tired, re·tir·ing.**

**rhythm** (riŦH′əm), movement that repeats evenly with a beat, accent, rise and fall, or the like: *the rhythm of dancing, the rhythm of music, the rhythm of the tides.* noun.

**rid·dle** (rid′l), a puzzling question, statement, or problem. EXAMPLE: When is a door not a door? ANSWER: When it is ajar. noun.

**roy·al** (roi′əl), of or about kings and queens: *We received a royal command to go to the castle.* adjective.

**rubber band** (rub′ər band′), a round, thin strip of rubber used to hold things together. noun.

**ru·in** (rü′ən), **1** building or wall that has fallen to pieces: *That ruin was once a famous castle.* **2** very great damage; destruction; overthrow: *The fire caused the ruin of many buildings. The king's enemies planned his ruin.* **3** destroy; spoil: *The rain ruined our picnic.* 1,2 noun, 3 verb, **ru·ined, ru·in·ing.**

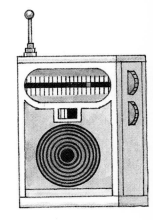

radio

restaurant

# S

**satellite**

**scales**

fish with **scales**

**scuffle**

**sat·el·lite** (sat′l īt), **1** a heavenly body that goes around a planet or other larger heavenly body. The moon is a satellite of the earth. **2** an object made by people and shot by a rocket into an orbit around the earth or other heavenly body. Satellites are used to send weather and other scientific information back to earth; they also transmit television programs across the earth. See picture. *noun.*

**sat·is·fy** (sat′i sfī), **1** give enough to; fulfill (desires, hopes, or demands); put an end to (needs or wants): *He satisfied his hunger with a sandwich and milk.* **2** make contented; please: *Are you satisfied now?* **3** pay; make right: *He satisfied all claims for the accident he caused.* **4** set free from doubt; convince: *She is satisfied that it was an accident. verb,* **sat·is·fied, sat·is·fy·ing.**

**scale**[1] (skāl) an instrument for measuring weight. It is usually called **scales.** See the picture. *noun.*

**scale**[2] (scāl), one of the thin, hard pieces that form the outside covering of snakes and lizards. See the picture. *noun.*

**sci·en·tist** (sī′ən tist), person who is an expert in some branch of science. Persons who are especially trained in biology, chemistry, mathematics physics, geology, and astronomy are scientists. *noun.*

**scuf·fle** (skuf′əl), **1** struggle or fight in a rough, confused manner: *The children were scuffling over the ball.* **2** a confused, rough struggle or fight: *I lost my hat in the scuffle.* See picture. **1** *verb,* **scuf·fled, scuf·fling; 2** *noun.*

**set·tle** (set′l), **1** agree upon: *Let's settle the question of what we're going to do.* **2** go to live somewhere: *The Pilgrims settled in Plymouth.* **3** be or put in a pleasant position: *The lost girl settled down in the big chair. verb,* **set·tled, set·tling.**

**set·tler** (set′lər), **1** person who settles. **2** person who settles in a new country. *noun.*

**shock**[1] (shok), **1** a sudden, hard shake or blow: *She felt the shock of the tree falling.* **2** something that upsets you suddenly: *The news is a shock to us.* **3** state or condition that a badly hurt person sometimes suffers. The skin of a person in shock feels very cold. **4** the feeling caused by an electric current going through the body: *She got a shock from the toaster.* **5** cause to feel shock: *His bad manners shock me.* 1-4 *noun,* 5 *verb,* **shocked, shock·ing.**

**shock**[2] (shok), a bushy mass: *My grandfather has a shock of gray hair. noun.*

**shove** (shuv), **1** push; move along by force from behind: *He shoved the chair across the floor.* **2** push against: *The people shoved to get into the hall.* **3** a push: *She gave the boat a shove into the water.* 1,2 *verb,* **shoved, shov·ing;** 3 *noun.*

**si·lence** (sī′ləns), **1** absence of sound or noise; stillness: *The teacher asked for silence.* **2** keeping still; not talking. **3** make quiet. 1,2 *noun,* 3 *verb,* **si·lenced, si·len·cing.**

**soar** (sôr), **1** fly at a great height; fly upward: *The eagle soared without flapping its wings.* **2** rise beyond what is expected or common: *Prices are soaring. verb,* **soared, soar·ing.**

**spare** (sper *or* spar), **1** keep from killing or harming: *Frost killed some flowers but spared others.* **2** get along without: *Father could spare the car, so he let me take it.* **3** extra: *Have you a spare tire?* 1,2 *verb,* **spared, spar·ing;** 3 *adjective.*

**spe·cial·ist** (spesh′ə list), person who works at one branch of study, business, or occupation. A heart specialist is a doctor who treats diseases of the heart. *noun.*

**sprint** (sprint), **1** run at top speed for a short distance. **2** a short race at top speed. 1 *verb,* **sprint·ed, sprint·ing;** 2 *noun.*

**squash** (skwosh), **1** press until soft or flat; crush: *She squashed the bug.* **2** game somewhat like handball and tennis. **3** the fruit of a trailing vine, used as a vegetable or for making pies. 1 *verb,* **squashed, squash·ing;** 2,3 *noun.*

**squeal** (skwēl), **1** make a long, sharp, shrill cry: *A pig squeals when it is hurt.* **2** such a cry. **3** inform on another. 1,3 *verb,* **squealed, squeal·ing;** 2 *noun.*

**stair** (ster *or* star), **1** one of a set of steps for going from one level or floor to another. **2** also, **stairs,** plural set of such steps; stairway: *the top of the stairs.* 1-3 *noun.*

**sta·tion** (stā′shən), **1** place to stand in: *A soldier has to stand at his station all day.* **2** place used for a special purpose. The places where soldiers live, where ships stay, and where policemen work are all called stations. **3** a special place to stop: *a bus station, a train station.* **4** one's place in a group: *Because he was new, he was placed in a low station.* **5** place: *She stationed herself at the door of the room.* 1-4, *noun,* 5 *verb.*

**stat·ue** (stach′ü), something made of stone, wood, metal, or clay that looks like a person or animal: *Almost every city has a statue of some famous person.* See picture. *noun.*

**stern·ly** (stèrn′lē), **1** harshly; firmly: *Our teacher frowned at us sternly. adverb.*

**stitch** (stich), **1** the loop of yarn that is made when you sew by moving a needle with yarn through cloth: *Take out these long stitches.* **2** sew; make stitches in: *The doctor stitched my cut. I stitched a patch on my shirt.* 1 *noun,* plural **stitch·es;** 2 *verb,* **stitched, stitch·ing.**

**straight** (strāt), **1** without a bend or curve: *a straight line.* **2** in a line: *Sit up straight.* 1 *adjective,* 2 *adverb.*

**stray** (strā), **1** lose your way; wander: *Our dog strayed from the yard.* **2** lost: *Don't bring any stray cats home.* 1 *verb,* **strayed, stray·ing;** 2 *adjective.*

**strength** (strengkth), **1** quality of being strong; power; force: *I do not have the strength to lift that heavy box.* **2** degree of strength; intensity: *Some flavorings lose their strength in cooking. noun.*

**stroll·er** (strō′lər), **1** a person who strolls; wanderer. **2** kind of light baby carriage in which a small child sits. See picture. *noun.*

**suit·case** (süt′kās′), a flat traveling bag. *noun.*

**syl·la·ble** (sil′ə bəl), a unit of pronunciation. Words are divided into syllables. *Word* has one syllable. *Sentence* has two syllables. *Paragraph* has three syllables. *noun.*

# T

**tear** (ter *or* tar), **1** pull apart by force: *Don't tear the page.* **2** be pulled apart: *Lace tears easily.* **3** a torn place: *She has a tear in her dress.* 1,2 *verb,* **tore, tear·ing;** 3 *noun.*

**tend** (tend), take care of; look after; attend to: *He tends shop for his parents. verb,* **tend·ed, tend·ing.**

**te·r·rif·ic** (tə rif′ik), **1** causing great fear: *A terrific earthquake shook Japan.* **2** very great or severe: *A terrific hot spell ruined the crops.* **3** very good; wonderful: *She is a terrific tennis player. adjective.*

**thou·sand** (thou′znd), ten hundred; 1000. *noun, adjective.*

**toe** (tō), **1** one of the five end parts of the foot. **2** the part of a sock or shoe that covers the toes: *I have a hole in the toe of my sock.* **3** touch or reach with the toes: *Toe this line.* 1,2 *noun,* 3 *verb,* **toed, toe·ing.**

statue

stroller

| a | hat | oi | oil | ə stands for: |
|---|---|---|---|---|
| ā | age | ou | out | a in about |
| ä | far | u | cup | e in taken |
| e | let | ů | put | i in pencil |
| ē | equal | ü | rule | o in lemon |
| ėr | term | ch | child | u in circus |
| i | it | ng | long | |
| ī | ice | sh | she | |
| o | hot | th | thin | |
| ō | open | ᴛʜ | then | |
| ô | order | zh | measure | |

**tornado**

**tortoise**

**watermelon**

**tor·na·do** (tôr nā′dō), a very powerful and destructive whirlwind. It comes down from a mass of dark clouds and moves over the land in a narrow path. See picture. *noun, plural* **tor·na·does** or *tor·na·dos.*

**tor·toise** (tôr′təs), **1** turtle with a high, arched shell that lives only on land.
See picture. **2** any turtle. *noun, plural* **tor·tois·es** or **tor·toise.**

**tough** (tuf), **1** bending without breaking: *Leather is tough.* **2** hard to cut, tear, or chew: *I couldn't eat the tough steak.* **3** strong; hardy: *a tough plant.* **4** difficult: *The heavy load was tough work. adjective.*

**traf·fic** (traf′ik), people, cars, wagons, ships, or the like coming and going along a way of travel: *Police control the traffic in large cities. noun.*

**T-shirt** (tē′shėrt′), a light, close-fitting shirt with short sleeves and no collar, worn for sports. *noun.*

# U

**u·nique** (yü nēk′), **1** having no like or equal; being the only one of its kind: *The astronaut described his experience as unique.* **2** very uncommon or unusual; rare: *His style of singing is unique. adjective.*

**u·su·al** (yü′zhü əl), commonly seen, found, or happening; ordinary: *His usual bedtime is 8 P.M. adjective.*

# V

**val·ley** (val′ē), low land between hills or mountains: *Most large valleys have rivers through them. noun, plural* **val·leys.**

**view** (vyü), **1** the act of seeing: *It was her first view of the city.* **2** see: *They viewed the ocean.* **3** the thing seen: *The view is beautiful.* 1,3 *noun,* 2 *verb,* **viewed, view·ing.**

# W

**wan·der** (won′dər), **1** move here and there without any special purpose: *We wandered around the fair, looking at exhibits.* **2** go from the right way; stray: *The dog wandered off and got lost. verb,* **wan·dered, wan·der·ing.**

**warn** (wôrn), **1** give notice to in advance; put on guard against danger or harm: *The clouds warned us that a storm was coming.* **2** give notice to; inform: *The whistle warned visitors that the ship was ready to sail. verb,* **warned, warn·ing.**

**wash** (wosh), **1** clean with water: *Wash your face.* **2** a bundle of clothes to be washed: *Put your socks in the wash.* 1 *verb,* **washed, wash·ing.** 2 *noun.*

**waste** (wāst), **1** make poor use of: *Though I had much work to do, I wasted my time doing nothing.* **2** poor use; useless spending. 1 *verb,* **wast·ed, wast·ing;** 2 *noun.*

**wa·ter·mel·on** (wô′tər mel′ən), a large, juicy melon with red or pink pulp and hard green rind. See picture. *noun.*

**wedge** (wej), **1** a piece of wood or metal with one thin edge, used to split wood. A wedge is driven into something that is to be split. **2** something shaped like a wedge. **3** squeeze: *His arm was wedged between two logs.* 1,2 *noun,* 3 *verb,* **wedged, wedg·ing.**

**wher·ev·er** (hwer ev′ər), where; to whatever place: *Please sit wherever you like. conjunction, adverb.*

**wis·ter·i·a** (wi stir′ē ə), a climbing shrub with large, drooping clusters of purple, blue or white flowers. See picture. *noun.*

**wor·ry** (wėr′ē), **1** feel anxious, troubled: *Don't worry about little things.* **2** make anxious; to trouble: *The problem worried her.* **3** to snap at, throw around with the teeth: *The dog worried the rug.* **4** trouble; care: *His worries made him unhappy.* 1,2,3 *verb,* **wor·ried, wor·ry·ing;** 4 *noun, plural* **wor·ries.**

**worth** (wėrth), **1** good or important enough for; deserving of: *That book is worth reading.* **2** value: *She got her money's worth out of that coat.* **3** quantity that a certain amount will buy: *He bought a dollar's worth of stamps.* 1 *adjective,* 2,3 *noun.*

# Y

**young** (yung), **1** in the early part of life or growth; not old: *A puppy is a young dog.* **2** young ones: *An animal will fight to protect its young.* 1 *adjective,* 2 *noun.*

# Z

**zone** (zōn), any region or area especially set off. A combat zone is a district where fighting is going on. *noun.*

| a hat | oi oil | ə stands for: |
|---|---|---|
| ā age | ou out | a in about |
| ä far | u cup | e in taken |
| e let | u̇ put | i in pencil |
| ē equal | ü rule | o in lemon |
| ėr term | ch child | u in circus |
| i it | ng long | |
| ī ice | sh she | |
| o hot | th thin | |
| ō open | ₮H then | |
| ô order | zh measure | |

**wisteria**

Section 2: Sharon Elzaurdia, 114; Judith Friedman, 81, 82, 84-87, 89-91, 93, 131; Carl Koch, 78, 95, 113; Elizabeth Miles, 115-117, 119-121, 123-128, 130
Section 3: George Armstrong, 138, 141, 142, 145; Lipman Design (Shawn Biner), 134; Charley Palmer, 132-133; Slug Signorino, 167; Jack Wallen, 151, 153, 154, 157, 159, 160, 162, 164, 185
Section 4: Christopher Blake, 209-211, 213, 217, 219, 220; Lisa Cinelli, 221-226; Ralph Creasman, 186-187; Judith Friedman, 206; John O'Brien, 191-203; Paul Ristau, 188, 189, 190, 227; John Sanford, 207
Section 5: Carole Byard, 281-287, 289, 290; Gretchen Mayo, 242-243; Leslie Holt Morrill, 247-257; Eileen Mueller Neill, 259, 260, 262, 264-267, 269, 270, 273-278, 292; William Peterson, 244; Paul Ristau, 279, 280
Section 6: Leon Bishop, 319-322; Judith Friedman, (border art) 326-341; Kay Fulton, 325; Roy Moody, 296-298; Stefan Platzer, 294, 295; Jack Wallen, 350
Glossary: Eilleen Mueller Neill, 367; George Suyeoka, 360-372

**Freelance Photography**
James Ballard, 22, 23

**Photographs**
Pages 76-77: Taken from TOWN & COUNTRY by Alice & Martin Provensen, Copyright © 1984 by Alice & Martin Provensen. Used by permission of Crown Publishers, Inc.; Page 99: Gabor Demjen/Stock, Boston; Page 101: James Blank/BRUCE COLEMAN INC., New York; Page 102: M. Feinberg/FPG; Page 103: (left) Eric G. Carle/BRUCE COLEMAN INC., New York; Page 103: (right) © 1985 Paul Light/Lightwave; Page 104: Jerry Howard/Positive Images; Page 105: (left) Lou Jones; Page 105: (right) © 1985 Paul Light/Lightwave; Page 106: Joe Viesti/FPG; Page 107: Dick Dietrich/FPG; Pages 108, 109: Bob Glaze/Artstreet; Page 110: Bob Daemmrich/TexaStock; Page 111: Steve Solum/BRUCE COLEMAN INC., New York; Page 139: James Jerome Hill Reference Library, Saint Paul, MN; Page 143: Neg. no. 323618. Courtesy Dept. Library Services, American Museum of Natural History; Page 144: Woolaroc Museum, Bartlesville, Oklahoma; Page 146: Courtesy Edward E. Ayer Collection, The Newberry Library, Chicago; Page 147: Georgia Historical Society; Page 148: Woolaroc Museum, Bartlesville, Oklahoma; Pages 209-211, 213-220: Photos by Alan Oddie. Copyright © 1979 by Lerner Publications Company. Reprinted by permission of Lerner Publications; Page 228: Museum of Modern Art/Film Stills Archive; Pages 229, 230: NASA; Page 231: Courtesy Hewlett-Packard; Pages 232-238: NASA; Page 245: Bill Eppridge/SPORTS ILLUSTRATED; Page 291: Photo by Jonny S. Buchsbaum. Courtesy Harper & Row, Publishers, Inc.; Page 318: Ernie Danek for Scott, Foresman; Page 348: Courtesy E.P. Dutton, Inc.

**Cover Artist**
"Washington Square Park" (detail) by Kathy Jakobsen © 1982. Photo courtesy Jay Johnson Inc. America's Folk Heritage Gallery, N.Y.C.

I. M. C.